Health for All

Health for All

A DOCTOR'S PRESCRIPTION FOR A HEALTHIER CANADA

Jane Philpott

SIGNAL
McCLELLAND & STEWART

Signal and colophon are registered trademarks of Penguin Random House Canada Limited.

Library and Archives Canada Cataloguing in Publication data is available upon request.

ISBN: 978-0-7710-1172-6
ebook ISBN: 978-0-7710-1476-5

Jacket design by Andrew Roberts
Jacket art: Arthimedes; New Africa; solution; Pixel-Shot; Monkey Business/stock.adobe.com
Typeset in Palatino Nova Pro by Daniella Zanchetta
Printed in Canada

Published by Signal,
an imprint of McClelland & Stewart,
a division of Penguin Random House Canada Limited,
a Penguin Random House Company
www.penguinrandomhouse.ca

1 2 3 4 5   28 27 26 25 24

 Penguin
Random House
Canada

For my mom and dad,
who taught me to care

Contents

Glossary of Abbreviations

AMC	Assembly of Manitoba Chiefs
CFS	Child and Family Services
CHA	Canada Health Act
CHC	Community Health Centre
CHT	Canada Health Transfer
CRENI	Centre de Récuperation Nutritionnelle Intensive
EMR	Electronic Medical Record
FNFAO	First Nations Family Advocate Office
FHG	Family Health Group
FHO	Family Health Organization
FHT	Family Health Team
FNMWC	First Nations Mental Wellness Continuum
HIAP	Health in All Policies
LTC	Long-Term Care
MHO	Matthew House Ottawa
MD	Medical Doctor
MP	Member of Parliament
MRP	Most Responsible Provider
MSF	Médecins Sans Frontières
MUAC	Mid-Upper Arm Circumference
NP	Nurse Practitioner

PCN	Primary Care Network
PHM	Participation House, Markham
PM	Prime Minister
PMO	Prime Minister's Office
PPE	Personal Protective Equipment
PSW	Personal Support Worker
RGP	Regular General Practitioner
SEAMO	Southeastern Ontario Academic Medical Organization
TRC	Truth and Reconciliation Commission
UNDRIP	United Nations Declaration on the Rights of Indigenous Peoples

Author's Note

The personal stories in this book are all true. Where I introduce a person with their full name, that is their real name. In other places, I start with only a first name. In those cases, I have not used the real name, and I have altered some personal information in order to protect the identity of those individuals.

Introduction

September 17, 2005—Zinder, Niger

We pull into the town of Bande in three vehicles marked Médecins Sans Frontières. Already a good-sized crowd is waiting. Truck doors open—boxes, tables, chairs emptied—and set-up begins.

I get out and greet several people, thank the driver, and begin to survey the crowd. Colourful, lots of chatter. Under each tree, where shade can be found, are groups of women and children. Multicoloured head scarfs—pink, blue, yellow. Women sitting on mats on the sandy ground. On each lap, a baby. Or so it seems. Many are old enough to be toddlers or preschoolers, but in size they resemble babies. The odd plump one in the lot. But most are thin. Some very thin. Many are fussy and irritable, although the heat of the day has only just begun. I look more closely to see if any are critically ill, any who cannot wait until the set-up is ready. It has not been uncommon in recent weeks for children to die even as they wait for help.

What do these women think about as they sit there? I try to imagine myself in their place—gathering with hundreds of other women from the village, finding my way in such a large crowd, seeking help for my child. What does it take for them to come to this place? Is there hope? Is there fear? I wonder how far they walked to get here and how many children they left at home. Is this a place of dignity for them? Is there solace in community as they wait here?

Then I look at the little faces. Some too unwell or too weak to look up. Many at the breast or asleep and snuggled up, wrapped on their mom's back. But some are bright-eyed and curious. I marvel at those strong, skinny ones. Thin wee extremities, ribs outlined above an inflated belly. Yet they are sitting up, determinedly picking away at the morsels in a tin bowl that sits on the ground in front of them. One child is particularly serious and contemplative. He sits—patient, peaceful, wise—like an old man who has lived through many trials and learned to accept them.

Meanwhile the pop-up clinic is nearly ready. The screener moves among the crowds with a plastic tape measure—determining the MUAC—the mid-upper arm circumference. If it is in the red or orange zone, the child is brought in for further medical assessment. Only the severely malnourished are admitted to the program. The MUAC red zone is a circumference of less than eleven centimetres. (Thinking about it later, I realize this is slimmer than the cardboard tube of a paper towel roll.) The women and babies move through the stations—weight, as they hang in cotton pantalons from a scale; height; temperature check; Paracheck, a rapid malaria test. Then lining up again to wait for consultation.

I look out—now seated at my consultation table—still trying to imagine life from the mothers' perspectives, wondering what it would be like if I had been born in their circumstances and they had been born in mine.

What is it like to grow up female in a country where less than 10 percent of women can read and write? I try to fathom being raised in a society where gender so profoundly dictates rights, responsibilities, and expectations.

I doubt that I would have survived the physical rigours of a woman's life in rural Niger, where I would likely have spent my childhood as a home assistant—gathering firewood, drawing water, carrying my siblings on my back.

Would I imagine other places in this world where seeking a doctor's consultation for my severely ill child is not exactly a community event? Would I sit there passively and stoically while some of the townspeople around me implied I was at fault for my baby's condition—that I was a simple "woman from the bush"?

I continue my consultations—interrupted by these questions in my head. And interrupted periodically to check on the sickest babies who have been placed in the salle d'observation.

I wonder how many we will see today. One hundred? Two hundred? Three hundred? More? Similar questions in Hausa each time. Zazzaɓi? Tari? Zawo? (Fever? Cough? Diarrhea?) Is she eating? Does she drink? And for those already in the program: Is she eating the Plumpy'nut? Two times per day? Plumpy'nut—the wonder food—adding weight and saving lives.

Eventually the day is done. All of the severely malnourished are given food supplements for the week and reminded to come back next week.

But the sickest are taken into the city to the CRENI (Centre de récuperation nutritionnelle intensive). These are the ones who really break your heart. They are so thin that as I lift a child while Mom adjusts her wraparound skirt, it's as if I am picking up a small skeleton. I feel the hip bones in my hand, with neither muscle nor fat to pad them.

Some are transported with a nasogastric tube in place to give some sugar water and treat the severe dehydration. Some are puffy. Some are somnolent. All are critically ill.

We arrive at the CRENI to deliver the new admissions—eleven today. It is troubling to watch—mothers and children, one by one, unloaded from the truck to the triage area. These young lives are quite literally fragile. Like emaciated porcelain dolls. Brittle. Dry. Heroically still breathing to keep alive in this world which seems to offer them so little. I take one in my hands to help, as his mom climbs down from the truck. He delivers a load of liquid feces into my hands and onto my skirt, which effectively grabs my attention and prompts me to move him up the line for a quick admission.

———

The paragraphs above are from a diary entry I wrote at the end of the first week of being stationed at Zinder, Niger, West Africa, on a mission with Médecins Sans Frontières (MSF). The people and events of that day, and others like it over the first two decades of my career, changed me on the inside. They unsettled me. The angst that was triggered by what I had seen was the birthplace of my vocation. The more I learned about the hunger, ill health, and other injustices that exist on this planet, the more I wanted to use what I had been given to make the world fairer. I was witness to the ways that inequitable social structures—in any country of the world—have an impact on people's health. I had to do what was within my grasp to alter those structures. In short, I became consumed by the pursuit of health for all.

When my husband, our children, and I lived and worked in Niger from 1989 to 1998, we became painfully aware that the world is not fair. We had done nothing to merit the multiple advantages to which we were born—just as those mothers I met in the town of Bande had done nothing to deserve the conditions that caused them and their children to suffer poor health and early death. During the years we lived there, I watched children die of starvation in a world that has plenty of food. Living in one of the poorest countries on earth taught me that while health is much more than health care, the people of Niger were terribly lacking in both.

I've spent most of my life in Canada, where we have a very different set of challenges and circumstances. But we are also far from achieving evenly distributed opportunities for people to be well. We are an affluent country, with abundant resources of many types. From the perspective of health services, we have a history of bold progress, such as the introduction of universal public health insurance, protected by the law. Yet as a result of several decades of denial, complacency, and neglect, our health systems are faltering.

I've observed the tenuous state of health systems at home and abroad over the past four decades—most of that time as a practising family doctor. I was also federal minister of health in Canada, in which role I co-led the negotiation of a health accord with our provinces and territories. More recently, I've been dean of the Faculty of Health Sciences at Queen's University, where we train the nurses, doctors, therapists, public health professionals, and researchers of the future.

It is from all those vantage points that I've become concerned about the well-being of Canada. Our health systems suffer from arrested development. After impressive progress in the last half of the twentieth century, Canada's health systems did not implement the full vision of the founders of medicare, which included universal publicly funded pharmacare, home care, long-term care, and dental care. Health systems stagnated under the weight of cowardice and short-sightedness. With our considerable assets, we can do better, and we need to do so quickly. Specifically, we should provide genuine access to primary health care for everyone. To do that, we must fortify our social and political structures—the deepest determinants of the health and well-being of Canadians.

Canadians who are currently in good health or who have never struggled to access health services might ask why they should care. The fact is, whether we can see the connections or not, our wellness is one of those things that is collective and interdependent. It was Martin Luther King Jr. who wrote, in a letter from a Birmingham jail, "Injustice anywhere is a threat to justice everywhere." In a similar vein, I believe that ill health anywhere is a threat to wellness everywhere.

Health for all matters for all. Canada's approach to health and health care must not become a case of the survival of the fittest, richest, or most well-connected. There is a negative impact on the whole country when some have easy access to healthy food, housing, and high-quality health care, while others slip further away from wellness in their daily lives and wait endlessly in the queue to access health systems. This growing inequality gap is a breeding place for anger, division, and political unrest.

Most parents are familiar with the sentiment that you can only be as happy as your least happy child. You know what it's like when one of your loved ones is suffering; until they are better, you cannot feel well. That's how I feel when people in our country cannot get the care they need. It drives me mad when I consider that six and a half million Canadian adults do not have a family doctor, or any other access to primary care.[1] Unless we act soon, it will only get worse. Our population is growing, rapidly in some provinces. The average age is rising. The health workforce is not keeping pace. It is insupportable to go on like this. Access to health care has been a long-standing, core Canadian value. It would be foolhardy to walk away from that value now. We can still work together to bring our health systems back from the brink.

The concept of interdependent wellness means our health depends on the health of others. Our experience of the COVID-19 pandemic made this clearer than it's ever been. Each of us was encouraged to protect ourselves from infection, not only for selfish reasons, but also because we could limit the spread of infection to people who would be most at risk of a severe or life-threatening case. We looked out for each other. We pulled together—at least for a while. This is no time to let go of our instincts for interdependence.

The fragile state of health systems in Canada is now the subject of daily dinner conversations and routine public discourse. Thousands of people have poignantly described their despair. Politicians have offered aspirational rhetoric about their commitment to see things improved. Unfortunately, we've heard little in the way of a concrete plan to reverse the descending spiral in which we find ourselves. Rhetoric has its place, but it is action that will change things for the better.

This book presents an off-ramp from that downward spiral and a way to fix a health system that is broken, and in which Canadians are losing faith. I describe four distinct but essential pillars that support a healthy society. Each part of the book is different in style and substance.

Part One is about the clinical foundation of health for all. It is about access to medical care—or lack thereof. This is the most prescriptive part of the book. It will appeal to students of public policy, but just as importantly, it should be of interest to anyone frustrated with faltering health systems. In it, I outline a proposal to disrupt and redesign health systems in Canada.

Part One is the most pragmatic section of this book, but it does not stand alone; it needs the other parts. We must do more than amend our clinical systems if we want to be a country in which everyone can be well. There are some underlying determinants of health that require attention in order for those clinical systems to be sustainable. I've chosen three other categories to address as well: spiritual, social, and political. The approach is holistic. To understand health, we must examine its roots and see the connections that exist within and among these categories.

Part Two changes gear and reads more like a memoir on well-being, including its mental and spiritual roots. Drawing on teachings that I learned from Indigenous people, the chapters are dedicated to hope, belonging, meaning, and purpose.

My own experiences provide the examples of how those factors contribute to wellness.

Part Three explores some of the social structures necessary for a healthy society. With stories from medicine and politics, I use case studies to examine the impact of social policies on the well-being of the country. The examples point to a range of social issues including housing, disabilities, and early childhood experiences as critical factors in attaining or sustaining wellness.

The final section, Part Four, is about politics—its power and potential in the pursuit of health for all. I investigate some of the multiple links between health care and politics—and conclude that Canadians should expect more from both. I borrow ideas from the clinical world to see how they could be used to mend the unhealthy parts of politics.

Finally, it should be said that the four parts of this book do not include *all* the essential underpinnings of a healthy society. For example, I do not tackle the fundamental importance of environmental health, and nor do I describe the technical or digital foundation that is essential to support health and health care. The scientific research required is another aspect I will leave for others to address. Suffice it to acknowledge that the foundations described herein are necessary but not exhaustive of the elements needed to uphold a healthy society.

I was a young doctor when I spent a decade living on the southern edge of the Sahara Desert, learning that the world is unfair, but feeling confident it could change. I was a middle-aged doctor when I wrote the diary entry that launched this introduction—still not dissuaded from believing that an acceptable level of health for every person on the planet is achievable. I'm older now. I've added political experience to my medical perspective, and I look at my own country—Canada—disturbed that even here, not everyone has acceptable access to care and the opportunity to be well. I refuse to give up the conviction that we can do better. I don't even think it's that hard. With a shared vision and relentless determination, we can care better for one another.

PART ONE

Clinical

CHAPTER 1

A Canadian Health Care Dream

Soon after Krista moved to Kingston, Ontario, in 2017, she began getting weird sensations of tingling in her feet. Being a bit frightened, and new in town, she went to the local hospital's emergency room. There, the doctor ordered an MRI of her brain. It showed a few abnormal spots, but they were not specific enough for a diagnosis. She was told to find a family doctor and arrange follow-up. In the months ahead, finding a family doctor proved to be impossible. Krista called every clinic she could find on Google; no one was able to help. She added her name to waiting lists. She had no option but to wait and see if the symptoms would go away.

But Krista's symptoms didn't resolve. In fact, she kept getting numbness off and on, as well as experiencing overall weakness. By 2020, just prior to the COVID-19 pandemic, the discomfort was enough that she returned to the emergency room. The doctor there repeated the MRI, which revealed that the spots were worse. A consultant said Krista might have multiple sclerosis, or perhaps a rheumatology problem such as lupus. She was referred to a neurologist, but by the time the appointment came around, that specialist had left town, and no one had taken on his patient load. She tried to get a referral to another neurologist but was unsuccessful.

Krista was back in the emergency department in 2023 for an unrelated problem. She was cared for by one of my Queen's University colleagues, Dr. Erin Brennan, who was distressed to see yet another person with chronic illness who had no access to primary care. Krista still hasn't received a firm diagnosis for her unresolved symptoms. She feels guilty for "bothering" the doctors in a busy setting where she sees someone different at every visit. She is finding it hard to work, and to care for two young children on her own. She asked Dr. Brennan for help navigating "the system" and wondered if someone in the emergency department might help her apply for disability support.

Krista's story, while concerning, is not dramatic. She does not have a condition that is immediately life-threatening. But she's not getting what she needs. My emergency department colleagues offer high-quality, compassionate care seven days a week, twenty-four hours a day. Until recently, emergency rooms were the backstop in our overstretched Canadian health systems—the open front door, available to everyone who walks in. But with staff shortages and a finite capacity when it comes to how many patients can be seen, that is no longer the case in many parts of the country. And the bottom line is that the emergency setting is not the best place for some types of care; for example, it should not be the only option for a person with a chronic illness who needs someone to care for them over time, as a whole person.

Dr. Steven Brooks, another emergency room physician and Queen's University faculty member, sent me a list of recent cases he's seen, to illustrate what it's like when people don't have a place to go for primary care.

- One man has worsening heart failure after years of uncontrolled hypertension.
- A woman has a giant abdominal mass that was not assessed by another physician because the only option offered to her was virtual care.
- A suicidal teen has no family physician and no other access to mental health supports.
- An older adult has confusion triggered by drug interactions. She is on more than twenty medications renewed by various emergency physicians and walk-in clinic physicians, but she needs a medication review by a primary care clinician.
- A man from a retirement residence has slowly declining cognition with no clear cause and requires the coordination of multiple assessments in the community.
- A young person is on opioids for chronic pain. Her high-dose narcotics get reordered without consideration of alternative non-opioid strategies because she sees different physicians at walk-in clinics and the easiest thing to do is renew the prescription.

- An older woman has falls, confusion, and a
  face that expresses no emotion—probably
  undiagnosed Parkinson's disease. She has
  no family physician and no social supports.
  A consulting neurologist offered follow-up in
  the movement disorders clinic, but that could
  take months. They advised to start levodopa-
  carbidopa. This medication requires close
  monitoring and dosage adjustment over time.
  Dr. Brooks asked her to start the medication
  and go to a walk-in clinic for reassessment.
  Given the woman's tenuous situation, he
  had an uneasy feeling that there wouldn't
  be proper follow-up.

Why do these people show up in emergency departments? The answer, in part, is that they may have no other place to seek help and they legitimately require health-related services. They are not alone. A 2023 survey called OurCare, led by Dr. Tara Kiran and her colleagues, estimated that about six and a half million adults living in Canada (roughly 22 percent of the adult population) have no family doctor, and no other access to primary care.[1]

Let's be clear at the outset that health is much more than health care. The *care* part is only the tip of the iceberg. We talk about it a lot because it's the part that is most readily visible. Health care includes hospitals, clinics, health professionals, prescriptions, medical devices, and other treatments. Some people suggest this collection of services should actually be called a "sickness-care system," and not "health care."

Regardless of what name we chose, we begin here with the clinical perspective because it is easier and more straight-forward to examine than the deeper factors that contribute to health. It might even be the part that is easiest to fix.

The positive news is that the stars are aligned to deliver the biggest disruption in Canadian health care since the introduction of medicare in the mid-twentieth century. The incentives have never been stronger: Journalists are sharing stories of people who have died because of inadequate access to care.[2] Health workers are bearing witness as the care systems fail to meet the needs of patients. A restless public is pleading for action from politicians.

Winston Churchill said that one must never let a good crisis go to waste. He spoke those words during the darkest days of the Second World War, when he and others could have suc-cumbed to despair but instead chose to forge new relation-ships and create better international structures for the future. Our circumstances are not the same as the fate of the Western world hanging in the balance, but these are indeed troubled days for health care in Canada—and around the world. We must use this health care crisis for good, taking a page from the past by forging new relationships and creating better structures.

The first step in fixing the status quo is to agree—and admit out loud—that it's malfunctioning. After a few years of assault from the COVID-19 pandemic, Canada's health care systems ought now to be in recovery mode. But we're not getting back on our feet the way we imagined we would. The pandemic exposed and exacerbated long-standing fault lines, and unless we do some hard work in the next decade to renovate our foundation, those cracks will widen.

Let's start by reviewing how bad things are. As noted earlier, 22 percent of Canadian adults do not have a family doctor. Emergency departments are being closed with unprecedented frequency. Thousands of health care jobs are unfilled. Health workers are exhausted and demoralized. Patients are waiting years to see some specialists. There is no national commitment for guaranteed access to home care, palliative care, or mental health care. And we still await the implementation of national pharmacare. All of this results in countless cases of delayed care, leading to both health harms and increased costs for Canadians.

Until recently, Canadians spoke with great pride about our health systems. We have laws from the last century to ensure universal insurance for medically necessary care—at least when that care is provided in hospitals or by physicians. Over the years, we have boasted about universal access to publicly funded health care—even though it has never actually been universal in terms of what is covered, and even though what is covered is not always accessible. As the people and places associated with care delivery have changed over the past six decades, our health laws and policies have not kept pace. As a result, the cracks in our health systems were forced wide open by the COVID-19 pandemic.

The way out of this is not a mystery. Health policy experts have written dozens of reports, over many decades, describing our vulnerabilities and offering solutions. Unfortunately, most of those solutions were never applied. Political parties make promises about employing some of the recommendations, such as pharmacare. And people in power speak about how they hope the system will improve in areas such as home care and mental health care. But hope is not a strategy. Aspiration is not operation. It has been decades since Canada has seen any government transform promises and wishes into implementation with universal fulfilment. Later, I will describe how some of that can be done.

We cannot fix all of the problems in health care overnight. We will have to prioritize, starting with a foundation based on primary care that has never been properly built in Canada. Simply put, we must make it a reality that every person living in Canada has a primary care home, just as every Canadian child has access to a public school.

The notion of a primary care "home" might not be familiar to everyone. It's not a home where you live, like a long-term care (LTC) or retirement home, but a health care setting where you *feel* at home—a place where you belong. The term is a variation of a concept called the *patient-centred medical home* that was introduced and made popular in the United States beginning in the mid-1990s. I prefer to use the term *primary care home*. This avoids the use of the word *medical*, and in doing so recognizes that what happens at your primary care home is more than medical. It also omits *patient-centred*; because primary care should *always* be person-centric, I believe that part of the phrase should go without saying.

I propose a system that guarantees *everyone* living in Canada has such a place to go. This may seem ambitious, but it is doable. It is smart. It is fair. The end state is more than universal coverage. It must be authentic access to care. Several provinces have done part of this work, but none of them have made it universal. And getting only part way is unacceptable. We would never tolerate a status quo in which only 80 percent of Canada's children were able to attend school.

Suggesting that the answer to our health system woes lies in primary care is nothing new. The best-known international consensus on the matter was achieved back in 1978 at a meeting in Alma-Ata—now known as Almaty, the largest city in Kazakhstan. At that time, representatives of 134 countries came together to declare that health is a fundamental human right and all governments should have a plan of action to launch and sustain primary health care as a part of their national health systems. In doing so, signatories to the Declaration of Alma-Ata agreed that "an acceptable level of *health for all* the people of the world by the year 2000 can be attained [italics added]."[3]

There it was. Almost fifty years ago, Canada was among the nations that knew and understood that the path to a healthier country runs through primary health care, including the services of primary care.[4]

Clearly, "an acceptable level of health for all people" was not achieved by the year 2000, not in Canada at least. A national health system rooted in primary health care is easier to describe than to achieve. Many countries cite challenges in acquiring the necessary funding, and there is no standard implementation protocol for universal access to primary health care.[5] Nevertheless, it must still be our goal. Scientific literature, including a landmark paper by the late Dr. Barbara Starfield and her colleagues in 2005, offers an abundance of evidence that countries with strong systems of primary care get the best health outcomes for their population, at the most affordable costs, in a way that is both equitable and accessible.[6]

The World Health Organization defines primary care as "a model of care that supports first-contact, accessible, continuous, comprehensive, and coordinated person-focused care."[7]

Every modifier in that definition matters. You might want to pause, reread them, and think about each one. Unfortunately, Canada has never intentionally designed or delivered a universal system of primary care. Perhaps we thought our good intentions would allow us to stumble into such a system, but clearly that hasn't happened. Thankfully, it is not too late.

In order to make this plan work, we need to get three groups of people on board: the public, the community of health professionals, and political leaders. The transition to universal primary care will happen faster if there is a shared vision with loud public demand for and expectation of such a system. We will not be successful unless clinicians are on board. Most of all, we will need the unrelenting determination of political leaders in all orders of government, of all stripes, who will fight for this vision on behalf of Canadians and not stop until it is accomplished.

The roots of Canadian medicare, our national health insurance plan, go back to 1947, when then Saskatchewan premier Tommy Douglas introduced North America's first universal hospital insurance plan—later adapted into a national program with the Hospital Insurance and Diagnostic Services Act of 1957. Later, doctors' services were added to the coverage, first in Saskatchewan and then nationwide with the Medical Care Act in 1966. Through those decades and later, when the original laws were amalgamated under the Canada Health Act (CHA) in 1984, there was plenty of opposition, especially from medical organizations. But medicare's champions persevered, including the Honourable Monique Bégin, who was federal minister of health and welfare when the CHA was passed with unanimous consent in the House of Commons. The result hasn't been perfect, but the CHA is the reason that, for the most part, Canadians receive the services defined as medically necessary care, within Canada, based on that need and not on your ability to pay.

While the CHA has largely withstood the test of time, it has not evolved with the changing health care ecosystem. It guarantees insurance coverage only for care provided either (1) in hospitals and/or (2) by doctors. Now, almost eight decades after medicare was just a dream in the mind of Tommy Douglas, most health care can or should happen outside hospitals, and we would be smart to insure the services of other health professionals who offer services in the community, in addition to doctors.

We have arrived at a critical point for a new generation of politicians willing to collaborate and do the hard work of implementing a national health service fit for our needs—a publicly funded system of primary care. It will save money and save lives. It could be called Medicare 2.0, the twenty-first-century transformation.

Let us start by painting a picture of the grand vision we can achieve.

Imagine it is 2035 and we are celebrating our collective success. After a decade of hard work, we can finally say that every Canadian has a primary care home. In each community, it is the front door to health care, the first location you call or visit unless you have a highly time-sensitive emergency. This is the place where the members of the care team know your name. They use it when they welcome your arrival with genuine warmth.

Your primary care home is staffed by a team that includes doctors, nurse practitioners (NPs), nurses, and administrators, plus others according to the specific community needs.

Some primary care homes have physiotherapists, occupational therapists, physician assistants, midwives, social workers, dieticians, pharmacists, and community paramedics. Where possible, the team is enhanced by the presence of health sciences students, as well as community volunteers. This is more than a collection of different health professionals and social service workers. They are more than the sum of their parts. They are trained to function as an integrated team in the delivery of care.

You have a long-term relationship not only with your family doctor but with that entire team of professionals. Your electronic medical record (EMR) is collated in one place. You and your other care-team members can access that information according to the permissions you set. If you move to a new community, and you grant permission, the EMR automatically, digitally, follows you.

Speaking of moves: If you do relocate, you are reassigned to a new primary care home based on geography, generally according to your place of residence. You do not need to beg for a family doctor or wait for years on a list of "unattached patients." Unless it's close by and you choose to return for care, you do not need to drive or fly back to your previous municipality to see the family doctor you had there. Your care is delivered close to home, ideally accessible within thirty minutes of where you live or work.

The doors of most primary care homes are open seven days a week, up to twelve hours a day. As the open front door—or the figurative first floor—of the health care system, these primary care homes offload pressure from emergency departments and enable hospitals to discharge their patients in a timelier way.

You can book appointments with your regular doctor or nurse practitioner for preventive care checkups or follow-up visits for chronic conditions. If you need to be seen on short notice, you can walk in for care. The triage team at the primary care home determines how quickly you need to be seen, and which clinician is right for you on that occasion. In some cases, care is offered virtually, as long as it is safe to do so. After your visit, you are encouraged to provide feedback by text message or on a website. This is used to improve the quality of your care experience and health outcomes, continuously and iteratively.

The primary care home is the coordinating centre for home care, including palliative care. When needed, someone from the team will see you at home or in the community, always ensuring the visit is linked to the primary care home and your records are updated in real time.

Where possible, your primary care home is a one-stop shop for other health-related services. This may include public health clinics or classes on topics such as nutrition, prenatal care, or mental wellness. Other specialist physicians are available to see you when they make regular visits to the local primary care home. Primary care homes also offer additional social services such as legal clinics, tax clinics, and mobility services. They are the heart of an integrated health system.

This may sound like a dream. This dream could be our reality.

It is a reality in the Netherlands, where more than 95 percent of citizens are registered with a family doctor.[8] If a patient moves, they can change, anytime. Visits and tests are captured in the patient's electronic record, which is accessible by other providers. The family doctor's office is the centre of the Dutch health system. Every family doctor offers care in their office or in the patient's home, and most teams include a manager, nurses, psychologists, and practice assistants who do both administrative and clinical tasks. Most palliative care is delivered by family doctors in the patient's home, in partnership with specialized nurses. After-hours care is provided at a "GP Medical Post" staffed by the family doctors from the surrounding practices and located in the neighbourhood hospital, making it easy to access specialists if needed.

Canadians can afford publicly funded universal access to primary care. In fact, it would be less expensive than what we are doing now, and it offers better value for the money spent. Those who say such a system is prohibitive financially have not done the math that includes the downstream savings. Based on work done with my colleagues in Kingston, Ontario, we have calculated that team-based primary care could be delivered for about $500 worth of government funding per person per year. That price tag *includes* the physician remuneration. If people don't have this care, the only alternatives are (1) to delay care, which means that the problem could get worse, causing it to be harder and more expensive to treat, or (2) to go to the emergency department. That trip, even before you add in the physician fees, will cost more than $300.[9] It's easy to see that every time the availability of a primary care home translates into someone being able to avoid a visit to the emergency department, we're saving money for the whole system.

Beyond better value for money in acute care, there are immense downstream savings with universal access to primary care. For example, you can avoid cancers or detect them early. It will also slow or prevent the onset of cardiovascular diseases such as heart attacks or strokes. Similar prevention of both costs and suffering could be described for every system of the mind and body.

So why does the scenario I've described above—or something like it—not exist? The reasons are historic and political. I will start with the history part and use my own experience as an example.

After graduating from medical school at the University of Western Ontario in 1984, I moved to Ottawa for specialty training in family medicine and later to Toronto for a fellowship in tropical medicine. For almost a decade, my husband Pep and I lived with our young family in Niger, West Africa, where I worked as a family doctor and a community health educator.

When our family returned to Canada in 1998, I started working as a family doctor at the Stouffville Medical Centre, northeast of Toronto, Ontario. At that time, family doctors were paid via a fee-for-service system. My assistant would submit a bill to the government for each patient encounter. The more patients you saw, the more you would be paid. This has some obvious drawbacks. There is an inherent incentive for doctors to bring patients back more often than they need to be seen. It would be rare for doctors to deliberately abuse that incentive, but seeing a patient more frequently than necessary can easily become the expected standard of care.

Soon after I started my practice in Stouffville, new models of primary care delivery were being developed and implemented, particularly in Ontario and Quebec. Policy-makers already understood that the fee-for-service payment model was not ideal.

In rapid fire, Ontario introduced a series of new arrangements beginning in 2002.[10] This started with Family Health Networks, followed by Family Health Groups (FHGs) and

Family Health Organizations (FHOs), and eventually Family Health Teams (FHTs). In a separate process, the province added Nurse Practitioner-Led Clinics in 2007. All along, there was another model of care in existence, the Community Health Centres (CHCs) that had been around since the 1970s, but these tended "to operate in lower-income neighbourhoods, and/or serve specific marginalized populations."[11]

With only a bit of healthy skepticism, my physician colleagues and I decided to transition from a fee-for-service system into one of the new models. In two family practice locations, I ended up being the administrative leader of the team. I helped the Stouffville Medical Centre become a FHG and then a FHO. Then, in 2008, I moved my practice to Markham and started a new FHO that also became a FHT.

For most people, this just sounds like alphabet soup. You need to be well-embedded and versed in primary care remuneration models to care about the nuances of each. But underneath all the acronyms, these primary care policies and practices have deep, tangible impacts on health care delivery.

Most of the options of primary care reform that became available in Ontario twenty years ago had one feature in common. There were lists of patients associated with each family doctor. In the United States, they often call this a *panel* of patients. In Canada, we usually call it a *roster*. An optional new payment system, known as a *capitation model,* was also introduced in 2002. The idea is to pay doctors a fixed amount per month to provide comprehensive care for an identified list of people, whether you actually see those patients or not.

This approach has some positive effects. In theory, the capitation model incentivizes keeping people well. It encourages doctors to address multiple problems at the same visit and to offer care by phone or email. The defined roster allows for proactive, population-based care. For example, data analysis can be used to show which patients have had the appropriate screening tests for cancers, such as pap tests or mammograms. Then you can contact those who are not getting preventive care and encourage them to be screened.

The capitation model was an attempt to remove the incentive in a fee-for-service system where the doctor would get paid more for seeing patients more frequently. The capitation model offers no material incentive for seeing patients more often than necessary, because you get paid almost the same amount for simply having a person on your panel, no matter how many times you see them.

Unfortunately, the model has some unintended negative consequences. Of course, every system will have room for abuse, but there are specific problems when you pay doctors according to the size of their roster. Most doctors only "sign up" the number of patients for whom they can reasonably provide care. On average, in Ontario, that's around twelve hundred patients per doctor.[12] There are a few doctors who build a very large roster, as much as twice the average size, but they may not be open for enough hours per week and nor have they hired other health workers to help manage such a large group of patients with the expected level of care. So, those patients technically have a doctor, and the public is paying those doctors to care for the whole group. And yet, in some cases, the patients can't get appointments. Meanwhile, the doctor faces minimal financial penalties for not providing access to care. In Ontario, among people who have a family doctor or primary care NP, only 40 percent report they can get a same-day or next-day appointment—and only 10 percent have access on evenings and weekends.[13]

Another big problem is that the formula pays almost the same monthly rate to care for a person of a particular age and sex regardless of what complex health conditions they may have. This creates a disincentive for clinicians to take on patients with chronic illnesses. The effect is that people who need care the most may struggle the most to find a family doctor who will add them to their roster.

Another key disadvantage of these models is less frequently identified but even more important. They are not universal. They divide the population sharply into haves and have-nots. Back in the pre-roster days, when I joined the Stouffville Medical Centre, our group felt a general responsibility to provide care for whomever showed up at our door. There was only one other small group of family doctors in the community, who cared for another set of thousands of patients. But between those two medical groups, the twenty thousand people who lived in Stouffville in the late 1990s pretty much knew, and even expected, that the family doctors in the town would offer care for the whole population.

As the town grew to its current size, it would have become impossible for those two groups of doctors to continue providing care for everyone. But the creation of rosters had the effect of limiting our sense of commitment. Rather than feeling an obligation to care for the whole community, we were only expected to provide access for the group of people on each doctor's list. I recall the day, probably around 2001, that we received (by snail mail) the printout developed by the

Ministry of Health and Long-Term Care. Thousands of names were listed on that old kind of printer paper that goes on and on for pages—one long sheet folding back and forth on itself with perforated page breaks. It was the ministry's way of assigning patients to an inaugural roster for each family doctor based on the data they had about which doctor a particular person usually saw.

Prior to that, we had an unwritten system of seeing the patients who needed to be seen and sharing the work among the group. It was fluid and organic. Among our team of five or six doctors, we pretty much knew all the families in each other's practices and the patients knew most of us. This happened because it was a small town, but also because we covered for each other on evenings, weekends, and holidays. Patients tended to develop a primary relationship with one provider, but if your regular doctor wasn't available, another one of us would step in, as needed. If someone new came to town, they didn't need to go around pleading to be put on someone's roster, they just showed up at the door, we pulled out a new file folder, and we started a chart. Perhaps I'm simply nostalgic for the good old days in a small-town practice. But in some ways, we did have better systems of population-based primary care prior to "primary care reform."

We had high hopes for primary care reform in Ontario. The new payment models made sense. But the results have been mixed and, with the benefit of hindsight, it's easier to understand why it was not a panacea. There was never a national plan for *universal* access to primary care—and not a clearly articulated provincial one either. Out of respect for the autonomy of physicians, there was never a requirement for family doctors to sign on to any of the reform options, although those of us who did were nicely rewarded financially. The allocation of FHOs was based purely on which groups of doctors decided to apply. It's fair to say the implementation plan was ad hoc.

One of the appealing features about the reforms in Ontario was that, for a while, we were finally going to be supported to work in interdisciplinary teams, through the introduction of Family Health Teams. We knew that many of the clinical activities of family doctors could also be performed by nurses or other professionals, who are less expensive and can conduct many of the procedures as well as or better than physicians can. But apart from the Community Health Centres, there was no public insurance to directly cover the costs of providers other than physicians outside of a hospital setting. Starting in 2005, FHTs were supposed to change all that. The FHT I started in Markham, Ontario (which happens to be called "Health for All"), has been a big success, and now offers care to about twelve thousand patients.

Unfortunately, the early experiment of team-based primary care in Ontario using the FHT was never applied universally. The decision was possibly linked to reports such as the one from the Institute for Clinical and Evaluative Sciences, by Rick Glazier and his colleagues, that showed how most of the resources for FHTs were going to look after relatively advantaged groups. It also showed that FHTs were not performing as expected to reduce emergency department visits.[14] The same study showed that CHCs, on the other hand, were serving more socially disadvantaged populations and were shown to reduce visits to the emergency room. Sadly, rather than amending the FHT model based on those findings, the experiment was frozen in 2012. Newer data reveals that team-based care does, in fact, reduce the use of emergency departments.[15] But the funding model is gone and today, about a quarter of the people of Ontario are fortunate enough to have access to an inter-disciplinary FHT.

Elsewhere in the country, there are very few publicly funded interdisciplinary teams. Quebec led the way with the intro-duction of multidisciplinary teams (Family Medicine Groups or Groupe de médecine de famille) in 2002. The province reports 65 percent of people are registered in a family medi-cine group.[16] This aligns with the OurCare survey, in which 29 percent of adults in Quebec report they do not have access to a family doctor or primary care NP.

Alberta adopted a Primary Care Network (PCN) model in 2005. By 2016, 80 percent of Alberta family doctors were part of a PCN,[17] but with the exception of a few places, the system could not be called interdisciplinary. A 2017 report by the auditor general of Alberta found there was only one non-physician for every four physicians in the PCN program. The report attributed this to the fee-for-service model that "provides little incentive for physicians to support and par-ticipate in these teams, because it pays only physicians and provides no funding for other healthcare providers in primary care" apart from a small number of nurse practitioners.[18]

We are a long way from access to team-based care for the entire country. To achieve that, we need a national standard for primary health care that doesn't currently exist. Individual family doctors (or even groups) cannot take on the health of the entire population as their professional responsibility any more than an individual schoolteacher should be expected to keep adding students to their classroom lists as the population of a community grows.

That said, primary care in Canada should function like public schools. Access to public school is one of the most universal social services standards that Canadians can count on. No one is left out. Children are assigned to a school based on their home address. If the population grows, a new school is built, and personnel are hired. The distance required to get to your local school may differ, but our Canadian experience and social contract makes it very clear that no child should be denied access to publicly funded education, until the end of secondary school.

When you move to a new community, you never need to question if your child will have access to a school. You may choose to send them elsewhere, but you don't have to worry about whether they will be on a school roster in a specific geographic area. And when you move to another town, you don't hang on to the link to your previous public school board out of fear that you'll never get connected to another one. Imagine if we had allowed public schools to be run the way we've allowed primary care to evolve. Imagine if we thought it was acceptable for millions of children to simply be on a waiting list to get access to education. Yet that's what we allowed to happen to primary care.

If we can design and implement universal access to public education, we can do the same for primary care. This should be our rallying cry.

CHAPTER 2

From Promise to Practicalities

One of the things I learned from my time in the federal government was how to move from an idea to a commitment to a reality. Those experiences give me confidence that our country can successfully implement universal access to primary care. The story that follows is one example of following through on a promise.

The first federal cabinet meeting I ever attended took place on an unusually warm autumn day, November 4, 2015. The new cabinet had been sworn in during a highly publicized morning ceremony at Rideau Hall. I was the newly appointed federal minister of health—the first and only medical doctor (MD) in Canada to be given this title. After the ceremony and a press conference, the cabinet ministers boarded mini-buses and found our way to a room on the second floor of Centre Block where cabinet meetings were held. The mood around the table was positively giddy. The tone was set by Prime Minister (PM) Justin Trudeau, who couldn't hide his smile. Given that the Liberal Party had been in third place going into the election, we were all still adapting to the shock of winning a majority mandate.

We found our assigned places and I was seated across from the PM. I was one of thirty-one ministers in total, gathered around a well-worn, solid-wood table built in the shape of a long oval. In a room where countless decisions of national significance had been made for decades, there was an ornate, dark, wooden plaque positioned unobtrusively above everyone's heads on the north wall, behind me. Using all-caps calligraphy, the plaque read: "LOVE JUSTICE, YOU THAT ARE THE RULERS OF THE EARTH." Those words are from the first verse of the Wisdom of Solomon, part of the apocrypha, a set of books published in the 1611 version of the King James Bible. Through all the meetings I ever attended in that room, no one ever pointed out the plaque or discussed it, but you couldn't miss it. Its command may have smacked of hubris, but the call to justice grounded me.

Two key matters were decided at that first cabinet meeting, both of which were announced within days of the decisions, so the agenda is not a great secret. The first decision we made as a group of ministers of the Crown was the restoration of the long-form census. Time was of the essence to get that off the ground so it could be implemented in 2016.

The second item for discussion was the establishment of an ad hoc cabinet committee on Syrian refugees. I looked across at the PM and listened carefully as he named the people who would be on the committee. To no one's surprise, the list included John McCallum, an experienced politician and the new minister for immigration, refugees, and citizenship. The PM named seven other members. Then, looking my way, he announced that I would chair the new committee.

Retaining my composure, all I could think was *holy crap*. I barely knew what a cabinet committee was, let alone what was expected for chairing one or, more practically, how we were going to deliver on the government promise to get twenty-five thousand Syrian refugees to Canada in a matter of weeks. Why did he think I would be able to do that? Don't get me wrong: I was thrilled to be given this task and fully committed to the issue. The effort to resettle Syrian refugees was one of the most important promises of the 2015 campaign, and one that I supported wholeheartedly.

That autumn, the entire country had been gripped by the plight of Syrian refugees, particularly after seeing the unforgettable image of the body of Alan Kurdi on a Turkish beach. The two-year-old boy had been one of sixteen people in a rubber dinghy attempting to cross the Aegean Sea from Turkey to Greece. Alan was among those who drowned after their vessel capsized. The boy's family was attempting to reach Canada and had been held up by paperwork problems in the process to be sponsored as refugees. A picture really does speak a thousand words, and what followed was a sudden outpouring of public sympathy for other refugees escaping war in the region. As a candidate in the federal election campaign, I was proud of Liberal leader Justin Trudeau when he made his promise about the number of Syrian refugees who would be brought in before the end of 2015, if he were elected. Of course, never did I think I would be chairing the cabinet committee tasked with overseeing progress on that promise.

While I'd never had the chance to lead in that exact capacity, I knew my inner resolve. I knew how to organize. I had helped to build health care organizations from scratch. I'd helped start medical education programs in Canada and in Ethiopia. This was one more health-related initiative, and I was determined that no amount of complexity would get in the way of making it happen. I had been asked to lead this committee, and on my very first day as a cabinet minister, no less. I would pour every ounce of my thinking, energy, and tenacity into the task.

The work of that committee, especially determining how we were going to orchestrate the process, was an enormously satisfying way to start my political career. We spent long hours evaluating countless iterations of the plan. I gained an immediate respect and awe for the role of the public servants who worked around the clock to figure out the logistics and how best to coordinate the multiple organizations that needed to be engaged. We developed a model so that several steps in the migration process (such as fingerprints, security screens, and medical examinations) that would ordinarily be done sequentially could be done in tandem, saving several weeks in our timelines.

The first plane of Syrian refugees arrived in Canada on December 10, 2015. I was one of several people, including the PM, who went to Toronto Pearson Airport to greet the new arrivals in an event heralded with substantial national pride. We hit the twenty-five thousand mark in February 2016, just a little beyond our deadline. And Canada has continued to offer sponsorship opportunities; to date more than seventy-five thousand Syrian refugees have been resettled to Canada since that first plane arrived.

Clearly, thousands of people were involved in this effort. I was merely one part of a larger operation. But I was proud of the fact that I could use my role as chair of the ad hoc committee to establish a tone of firm resolve. We were determined to get the job done.

—

While the task of bringing tens of thousands of Syrian refugees to Canada was complicated and complex, to be sure, it is modest in comparison with the work of overhauling and redesigning health systems in this country. Even so, there are fundamental lessons one can take from the Syrian refugee project to demonstrate what will need to happen to achieve the goal of universal access to a primary care home.

Some say health is the business of provinces, which will never tolerate federal intervention. I say we are all Canadians. The consequences of poor health care do not respect domestic, or even international, borders. Canadians do not care which level of government writes the cheques. They want better results for the money. The Syrian refugee resettlement shows that when governments want to do transformative once-in-a-generation projects, when they have a clear and measurable goal, and when they have public support and political determination, their co-operation results in a beautiful thing. I was part of that. I saw it with my own eyes.

In that experience with the successful migration of Syrian refugees, these were the ten conditions that made such a project possible:

1. Leaders understood and articulated a problem of national relevance.
2. Leaders understood and articulated a shared vision with a measurable end result.
3. Canadians demonstrated broad support for fixing the problem.
4. Leaders could point to how Canadians and others would benefit from fixing the problem.

5. The federal government had the authority to lead on solving the problem.

6. Provincial governments chose to collaborate with minimal squabbles about jurisdiction.

7. Regional and municipal leaders were engaged and prepared to help.

8. Canadians and communities were willing to pitch in with many types of support.

9. Governments exhibited a willingness to realign bureaucratic policies and processes.

10. The federal government set the goal, developed the overall plan, and saw it through.

A study of these success factors in Syrian refugee resettlement could be a clue to solving the problem of lack of access to primary care.[1] Applying them might look something like this:

1. Leaders understand and articulate a problem of national relevance.

The problem of lack of access to family doctors or other primary care clinicians is huge and growing. It has been quantified. Based on the OurCare survey cited earlier, we can confidently estimate that six and a half million Canadian adults do not have a family doctor or a primary care NP.[2] That's about one person in five. But in some parts of Canada, it is almost one in three who lack such access. This means you or someone you know does not have access to primary care. The ripple effect of this patchy access is less well understood, but suffice it to say that until we have a firm foundation of primary care, the rest of our health systems will be less efficient and less effective.

2. Leaders understand and articulate a shared vision with a measurable end result.

We have work to do on getting leaders to articulate a shared vision. In recent federal and provincial election campaigns, there have been references to ensuring that everyone would have a family doctor. Occasionally, this has included the concept of a primary care team. New money offered by the federal government in 2023 is expected to support those aspirations. Up until now, there have been sporadic efforts by provincial governments to increase access to primary care teams, but so far, no province has committed to, let alone implemented, a plan to make them available to everyone. This may be the biggest challenge we face.

The good news is that with the right tools, we can build in accountability. If the shared vision is universal access to a primary care home, it's measurable. We will know when we get this right. Having a universal guarantee makes it easy to know when that goal has been reached. Nothing short of 100 percent will do.

3. Canadians demonstrate broad support for fixing the problem.

Almost daily, we read news articles about the lack of access to care. We hear about it from neighbours and colleagues. People I've never met send me email messages, such as this one: "My doctor is one of the six (in our city) retiring next month, and I have to say I have been in panic mode, along with all the thousands in the same position. One doesn't anticipate how scary it will be to not have a family physician until faced with that reality."

Public polling confirms that Canadians are having trouble accessing primary care and they are concerned. A 2023 survey of five thousand people by the Angus Reid Institute in partnership with the Canadian Medical Association revealed that *half* of the respondents either didn't have a family doctor or were finding it difficult to get an appointment with the one they have.[3] The overall results of the survey paint a dismal picture about the state of health care, and two-thirds of the respondents were pessimistic about the prospect that things will improve in the next two years.

It is not just individuals who care about this problem. Businesses also recognize that people do not want to move to a new location in Canada unless there is some kind of assurance that their family will be able to access primary care.

The more people speak publicly about the importance of this problem, the better. A well-heard collective public voice is a key to fixing it, though the methods for clearly discerning the public mood may be limited. In the case of the Syrian refugee crisis, the electoral mandate achieved in the 2015 election was the affirmation the government needed to implement a national initiative. I would like to see upcoming election campaigns, federally and provincially, with a platform that includes a commitment to universal access to primary care. It would give the public a chance to talk with their vote—and it would give the incoming government the mandate needed to move ahead and implement primary care for all.

4. Leaders can point to how Canadians would benefit from fixing the problem.

When people are sick and can't get access to primary care, a few different scenarios can ensue. Sometimes people get better on their own. It's great when that happens. But often, the condition gets worse. If someone is sick and can't be seen by a primary care team, they will eventually seek help at another location, often an emergency department. As explained earlier, the cost of one emergency department visit may be higher than the entire annual per capita cost of running a primary care home. Every time a visit to your primary care home prevents you from needing to visit the emergency department, we've saved public funds. The other scenario that happens when people don't have access to primary care is that they delay or defer their care. This means that some illnesses, including serious conditions like cancer, are not detected as early as possible. In some cases, the delayed treatment will be less effective, more complicated, or more expensive.

Recently reported research through the United Kingdom's National Health Services (NHS) offers a stunning look at the potential savings from providing better primary and community health care. Based on five years of data, the report concluded that "For every £1 that is put into 'upstream' NHS services in places with historically poor funding, including primary care settings such as GPs' surgeries and wider community treatment, there is a return of up to £14 to an area's Gross Value Added (GVA) output."[4] The returns on investment were attributed to reduced illness, improved health outcomes, and a more productive workforce, as well as job creation. Clearly, Canadians would also benefit from greater investments in primary care.

So, the first four conditions for success have been met in the case of the bold vision of universal access to a primary care team. The remaining conditions are more challenging.

5. The federal government has the authority
to lead or co-lead on solving the problem.

There's nothing stopping a province or territory from implementing universal access to primary care right now. Provinces
have the jurisdictional authority to do so. So why does the
federal government even need to be involved? In fact, many
people will argue that this is not the federal government's business. Isn't health care a matter for the provinces to handle?

Those are good questions, and the answers are key to getting this problem solved. However, it is time to stop perpetu-
ating the myth that health care is a purely provincial matter.
Every time you hear someone say that health is not the business of the federal government, I suggest you challenge them
on it. In fact, you might want to note what the Supreme Court
decided in 1982, when questions like this arose. Their answer
was that "health is not a matter which is subject to specific
constitutional assignment but instead is an amorphous topic
which can be addressed by valid federal or provincial legislation, depending in the circumstances of each case on the
nature or scope of the health problem in question."[5]

When it comes to the division of power, authority, and
responsibility over health and health care, it's fair to say these
are shared. That is, the federal, provincial, and territorial
governments all have a role to play. I would add to this and
clarify that Indigenous governments could also exert jurisdiction over health, even if it has not been done before now.
Regional and municipal governments may also deliver services such as public health. Ideally, all orders of government
would work together—and Canadians want, not to mention

need, them to do so. If actual collaboration is impossible, every order of government can still contribute to the goal of primary care for all. No government should be off the hook with worn-out excuses about jurisdiction.

My strongly held belief—influenced and emboldened by my time as minister of health—is that when it comes to a grand vision like implementing universal access to primary care, we need to stick together and be a nation. We are one country, after all, not simply a collection of provinces and territories divided by geographical interests and regional demands.

I'm far from the first person who has said the federal government should play a leadership role in the restructuring of health care in Canada. This was a key conclusion in a landmark study by the Standing Senate Committee on Social Affairs, Science and Technology, led by Senator Michael Kirby. Tabled in the fall of 2002, the Kirby report was the result of two years of work by the Senate committee, after listening to hundreds of witnesses. Their final report upheld the legitimacy of the federal government's role in health. This was in part because of the federal opportunity to harmonize health systems and set countrywide standards. But it also made the obvious point that, given the massive sums of money transferred from the federal treasury to provinces and territories, taxpayers would expect "that the federal government has a seat at the table when restructuring of the health care system is discussed."[6]

Given that the Kirby Report was tabled two decades ago, it's fascinating to read how Canadians were tired of the finger-pointing and blame-laying between governments over their contributions to health care. If we were impatient then, I'm not sure how to describe the public frustration now, after more than twenty years with so little progress to show for the recommendations of the report.

As if one major government report in 2002 were not enough to offer advice about the status of health care, it was only one month later that the Romanow Commission tabled its final report in the House of Commons, entitled *Building on Values: The Future of Health Care in Canada.* Roy Romanow had completed a decade as premier of Saskatchewan when he was asked to lead that Royal Commission. He was and remains a champion of publicly funded care—and it should be noted that this former provincial leader has been a staunch advocate for federal–provincial co-operation on matters of health.

While there are policy differences between the reports, they align on the value and legitimacy of federal leadership. The Romanow Report explicitly included a call to stop the inter-jurisdictional squabbling and get on with the work of improving health care. Here's what it said:

> The time has come for governments to focus on
> a collective vision for the future, rather than the
> jurisdictional or funding issues that have been the
> focus of intergovernmental debate for much of
> the past decade. This collective vision must focus
> on achieving effective reform and modernizing the
> system. It must reflect the priorities of Canadians.[7]

6. Provincial governments can collaborate with minimal squabbles about jurisdiction.

We can point to Senate committees, royal commissions, and the Supreme Court to make the point that health is a shared jurisdiction. This is not to deny, however, that provinces and territories have the dominant role in the operations and delivery of health systems.

Globe and Mail journalist André Picard gave a guest lecture at Queen's University early in 2023. During the discussion after his talk, in response to a question about jurisdiction, he emphasized the point that there is no constitutional barrier to collaboration. Hear, hear. Canadians expect politicians to co-operate across jurisdictions on matters of health, for the good of the country. They did so in the early months of the COVID-19 pandemic. They should do so to address the chronic barriers to better care.

It should be said that provinces and territories could implement universal access to primary care on their own, though the political will is not obvious. Across the country, to date, there is no province whose leaders have made a commitment to make primary care teams available for everyone—despite the evidence, and despite the outcry from Canadians, health workers, and health policy advocates. There is nothing stopping provinces from acting immediately to make it happen. How should we interpret the fact they have not yet done so? Could it be they do not know the evidence? Or they are distracted by the expensive parts of health care (hospitals, doctors, and drugs)? Or they lack the ambition and courage to transform their region in a way that will save money, save lives, and optimize the health of the population? Perhaps no government thinks the implementation of universal access to primary care will help them win the next election. Unfortunately, good public policy is often not seen to be politically expedient. At worst, in the case of health care, it is sometimes even regarded as polit-ically dangerous—a third rail no political party wants to touch for fear of losing votes.

A less cynical interpretation of why provinces and territories haven't guaranteed a primary care home in every neighbour-hood is that the national standard and expectation has yet to be established—at least in legislation. That's what we need now. I'm convinced that the federal government can establish the plan, and then support provinces and territories on imple-mentation, with minimal squabbling.

In the past, provincial leaders have found it convenient to perpetuate the notion that matters of health are almost entirely under their jurisdiction. This has sometimes been the case when the federal government has an interest in the sharing of data or the standardization of health outcome metrics. For example, this was frustrating when I was federal minister of health and realized how difficult it was to get national-level answers to questions such as: How many opioid-related deaths occur each month across the country? In 2016, no one could provide an answer, other than waiting until Statistics Canada updated its mortality data, which lagged by two years. We were finally able to get reliable data on the question, but it took months of hard work and the convening of provincial coroners and medical examiners to agree upon standard definitions of what constitutes an opioid-related death. It took more work to extract some willingness from each province and territory to report this information to the federal government. What kind of country can't even get reliable, timely data about how many people die and from what cause?

It turns out the federal government has tools at its disposal to compel the co-operation of provinces. The most obvious is its ability to make laws and regulations. When I was in government, we used these tools when we introduced a legal framework around medical assistance in dying (MAID). In fact, the law we wrote requires the federal minister of health to make regulations about "the provision, collection, use, and disposal of information regarding requests and provision of MAID in order to monitor the practice."[8] A set of regulations followed the passing of the laws about MAID, making it clear that the federal government could and would expect provinces and territories to collect personal information for the purpose of monitoring the impact of the MAID law.[9]

Another powerful device at the disposal of the federal government is something called federal spending power. This is a fascinating concept, and not difficult to comprehend. Federal spending power means that *if* there is reason to assume a broad national consensus on a matter—such as an electoral mandate—the federal government can initiate cost-shared programs in areas ordinarily considered to be provincial jurisdiction by giving money to provinces with strings attached.[10] There has to be a mechanism for provinces to opt out if they don't want to participate, and they can potentially be reimbursed if they agree to run a comparable program.

It is thanks to this instrument of federal spending power that Canada established medicare in the first place in the mid-twentieth century. One person who was involved in that, and wrote about it extensively, was the late Tom Kent. His name and legacy are not well known to most current political watchers, but when he died in Kingston in 2011, he was described as Canada's foremost activist-intellectual.[11] I never knew him, but I wish I had. He was an advisor to Prime Minister Lester B. Pearson, and then later in life was a Fellow at the School of Policy Studies at Queen's University. Kent's views on federal spending power are instructive, as he explains that "Canada's social programs were not created by federal dominance over provincial jurisdiction. They were created by federal and provincial governments in consensus driven by democratic will, by a tide of public opinion."[12] I like to imagine that someday—not far off—we will describe the transition to a Canadian universal right to primary care in exactly the same way.

Every year, the federal government sends a huge amount of money to the provinces and territories for health care. The largest chunk of that money is called the Canada Health Transfer (CHT). In 2023–24, the CHT was $49.4 billion. When that money is transferred to provinces, the only string attached is the requirement to abide by the principles of the Canada Health Act. To be sure, that's a thick and important string. It's the mechanism by which the federal government can (technically) make sure that Canadians will get access to medically necessary care based on their health needs and not on their ability to pay for care.

The size of the CHT grows every year and, lest we forget, this money comes from Canadian taxpayers themselves. It's not the government's money. It's our money. The government is the steward of those funds. Apart from adhering to the CHA, the federal government has never added any additional conditions or requirements about how the money should be spent.

In 2016, when I was health minister, we agreed to send the provinces a large infusion of funding (in addition to the CHT) that nominally had conditions attached. That is, we expected the money to be spent on home care and mental health. Since then, the bureaucracy has worked hard to develop metrics intended to show that Canadians have had better access to both of these things as a result of that influx of funding. But it might take a degree in health policy and an enormous amount of time wading through data at the Canadian Institute for Health Information[13] to get a clear idea about whether that investment achieved what it was designed to do. Needless to say, it's not easy to show that it improved access to care. Returning to the wisdom of Tom Kent, this kind of block funding "is not in any event a sound basis for an effective, steady program."[14] In retrospect, I regret to admit he was right. The block funding for mental health and home care did not make the most valuable use of the federal spending power, and I'm not aware of any universal programs to show for it.

Surely there is a way that federal spending power can be used more effectively. Let's consider how it could be directed to implement the vision of becoming a country with universal access to primary care. How could we make this work across the whole country when the provinces are largely responsible for the delivery of care? There are a few options.

A simple use of the federal spending power would be for the federal government to fund primary care teams directly in a province or a region, as a demonstration of universal access for a defined geographic area. This could be particularly helpful if it included support for evaluation of comparable models, so as to answer questions such as:

- Which health professionals should be part of the national standard for care teams?
- How many primary care homes are needed for a given population?
- What technical and administrative infrastructure is required?
- What is the return on investment?

This would be a step in the right direction, but we must get beyond our habit of being a nation of pilot projects. We need a countrywide plan. Given the absence of a proactive commitment by provinces and territories, it's time for the federal government to legislate a requirement for those provinces and territories to develop and implement systems of universal access to primary care. Other countries, whose health systems are better rooted in primary care than ours, have achieved this through the underpinning of federal legislation. What I propose for this purpose is something called the Canada Primary Care Act. Consider it a sister act—inspired by the CHA.[15] If you've never looked at the CHA, you might not know how delightful it is in its simplicity and clarity. It is divided into these sections:

- Purpose
- Cash Contribution
- Program Criteria
- Conditions for Cash Contribution
- Defaults
- Extra-billing and User Charges
- Regulations
- Report to Parliament

When written in both French and English in columns side by side, the CHA is only fourteen letter-sized pages long. It's one of those rare pieces of legislation that received unanimous support when it was passed in Parliament in April 1984. It's the perfect model for the Canada Primary Care Act. You set out the principles in the program criteria so Canadians know what they can expect. Commit to federal investments. Make it clear that if provinces are non-compliant, the federal contributions will be reduced or withheld.

The federal government could use its spending power to link a portion of the CHT—or better still, a separate transfer—to primary care. The new law would establish the overall goal: universal, authentic access to primary care. The provinces could determine how that access would be delivered. Dedicating a portion of the federal transfer to this cause would give Canadians a mechanism for accountability. This would not require fancy metrics or the need for Canadians to sort through information databases. All it would take is a simple process by which Canadians could report that their region has not yet provided them with a primary care home. To the extent that such accounts were reported, there would be a meaningful claw-back of funds to the province, thereby giving them the incentive to establish or restore universal access.

We should look to other countries for additional accountability mechanisms. For example, Norway has a set of laws, including the Patients' Rights Act, that establish the right of access to primary care. A network of health ombudspersons in fifteen regional offices offers an avenue for complaints about access to primary care. While these mediators do not have disciplinary power, they do have the power to investigate and raise issues to a higher level if the issues appear to be systemic. This works because the accountability is enshrined in legislation, and it is strengthened both by contracts with family doctors to document their obligations for access to care as well as a commitment from municipalities to add clinical services if the existing providers cannot meet the local need.

7. Regional and municipal leaders are engaged and prepared to help.

This was one of the most inspiring aspects of the national project to resettle Syrian refugees. It was impressive to see the way that regional and municipal leaders became engaged. They hosted roundtables and welcoming events. They could see their communities would benefit by bringing in new residents and future citizens.

When it comes to health care, Canadian communities have shown a range of responses from regional and municipal leaders. Increasingly, Canadian cities have been providing incentives to attract health workers. This has been manifested by sign-up bonuses for family doctors who come to a community and agree to stay for a designated period of time. Other innovations could include communities coming together to welcome nursing students, medical students, and others who do their placements in local clinics, perhaps offering subsidized furnished accommodations.

There is an enormous opportunity for local leaders to do more. It is well-known that businesses take an interest in whether or not their potential employees will be able to access primary care. The introduction of primary care homes in every geographic neighbourhood of the country opens up countless ways in which municipalities could be partners in the delivery of better care.

Canada and its provinces could be more creative about the role of municipalities in health care. Looking to Norway again, each of its 356 municipalities is entirely responsible for primary care delivery. They introduced the "Regular GP (RGP) Scheme" in 2000 as the basis for their system. The regulation says that "Any resident in a Norwegian municipality has the right to be registered with an RGP."[16] In a later section, the regulations put accountability in the hands of the municipality if a person's rights are violated by inadequate access to primary care.

8. Canadians and communities are willing to pitch in with many types of support.

Governments often forget to activate the most expansive and powerful resource available to them—their people. In the case of welcoming Syrian refugees, this was the most heartening part of the entire national project. In hundreds of municipalities across the country, civil society came together to participate. Neighbourhoods, clubs, faith groups, schools, and families rallied their resources to sponsor refugees, to collect clothing, and to create jobs. They hosted welcome events. They learned about Syrian culture, faiths, and languages. They raised money. They celebrated the arrival of families from an entirely different part of the world because they believed it was both honourable and enriching to do so.

We should harness this exceptional resource in the creation of a national model of primary care homes for everyone. The people of Canada are ready, willing, and able to serve their communities because they understand that this is what it means to be a civilized society. We saw this kind of community spirit at the height of the COVID-19 pandemic as people responded to public health directives not just to protect themselves but for the good of their community. When I imagine primary care homes in every community, I imagine the impressive workforce of community volunteers who will not only contribute to care delivery but will find meaningful activity and a place of belonging for themselves.

9. Governments exhibit a willingness to realign bureaucratic policies and processes.

It's one thing for politicians to announce a redesign of health systems; it is quite another to set the ambitious goal of universal access to primary care. Its implementation requires government officials in the relevant ministries or departments to have the right structures and support to make it happen. The bureaucracy—the machinery of government—will need to be efficient, effective, and enthusiastic for this transformation to be successful.

I'm fully aware that the very word *bureaucracy* evokes a sea of red tape, not to mention slow, often ineffectual processes. It may conjure a vision of office workers who are overly pedantic, bound by the absurd number and nature of rules and regulations that allow them to stall and frustrate ordinary citizens who are simply looking for government services to respond to their needs. In my experience, government bureaucrats excel at following the instructions and pace set by politicians. When they are being slow, obstructive, and seemingly irrational, they may be responding to deliberate directives that have not been communicated to the public. An alternate explanation may be that their performance expectations have not been set and monitored.

On the contrary, when political leaders are directing them to be creative, find solutions, rewrite the policies, and enact the regulations, government officials are experts at doing so. In fact, in some circumstances, they've been waiting for someone with authority to let loose the bonds that hold them back. This is what happened in the welcoming of Syrian refugees. Bureaucrats were given free rein to innovate, to align their procedural steps for migration, and to speak up about new ideas on how the government could successfully meet its targets.

That same spirit of ingenuity could make a huge difference in implementing a national system of primary care homes. There will need to be realignment and coordination within ministries of health to put greater emphasis and resources into primary care. (And to make the whole thing sustainable, cost savings must be found elsewhere.) In practical terms, the operations and oversight of the system would not reside within government but should be delegated to an arm's-length health authority—similar to the way school boards function, independent of the Ministry of Education.

10. The federal government sets the goal, develops the overall plan, and sees it through.

A federation such as Canada offers tremendous autonomy for provinces, territories, and self-governing First Nations. This enables variability so that programs and services meet the unique needs of each region. But the federal government should not abandon its responsibility to create the overarching plans and set national standards. In the best interests of the country, the federal government must set the goal of primary care for everyone, and then back it up with the right combination of carrots and sticks to make it a reality.

In the case of welcoming Syrian refugees, the government's goal was a SMART one—specific, measurable, achievable, relevant, and time-bound.[17] The campaign promise, as I stated earlier, was to bring twenty-five thousand Syrian refugees to Canada by the end of 2015. We missed that deadline by a few weeks, but otherwise the goal, the plan, and the execution were a huge success, and everyone knew it.

Applying the same kind of criteria for transforming health systems across the entire country may be a bit of a stretch—but let's see how it might look.

I've been clear from the beginning of this book that the **specific** goal would be to ensure that every person living in Canada would have access to a primary care home, in the same way that every child has access to a public school. The repetition of that goal is entirely intentional. I want it to soak into our national fibre the more we state it, until politicians have no choice but to act on it out of political expediency and because it simply makes sense.

This is **measurable**. Because the goal is universal access, it should not be difficult to know if it's been achieved. If the goal were to ensure that 80 percent of Canadians had a primary care home, that would be much harder to measure. You'd have to count the number of primary care homes and then how many people were rostered to each home, and then somehow calculate the number of people remaining outside the system. That's essentially what we have now—and no one is exactly sure how many people lack access—even with the 2023 OurCare survey estimating it's about six and a half million Canadian adults.

But 80 percent is not good enough. Nor is 85 or 90 percent. We need 100 percent. Government agencies can develop a reporting mechanism for those who do not have access—and a system to assign each person to a primary care home. Recall that school boards easily assign children to a public school. This is not hard *if* we are collectively determined to do it and we allocate resources to the right places.

I am fully convinced that with the right kind of political leadership, this goal is **achievable**. It will require restructuring. It will require significant early investments to establish and outfit the new care sites and hire teams of health workers. The return on investment will be substantial.

One potential barrier is the need for buy-in from doctors and their medical associations, which wield remarkable power. Doctors enjoy significant autonomy, such as choosing where to practice and even choosing which types of patients they're willing to see. Most Canadian family doctors have not worked in a system where they share the responsibility of caring for *all* the people within a geographic boundary. I take encouragement from a survey of recently graduated physicians showing the majority were "willing to practice with reduced clinical autonomy in exchange for a salaried compensation model that includes health benefits, pension, vacation time, and other benefits."[18] Even so, managing the power and independence of physicians could be a challenge. The solutions may involve some of the following:

- a marked increase in the physician supply—
  ideally through expanding medical education
  in Canada rather than poaching physicians
  from other countries—thereby making the

physician workforce less of a "sellers' market";
- incentives for medical graduates to become family doctors;
- incentives for family doctors to work in salaried models and teams that provide care for everyone in a geographic region;
- legal mechanisms to prevent doctors from establishing parallel private-pay health systems; and
- political courage, the likes of which Tommy Douglas, John Diefenbaker, Lester Pearson, Monique Bégin, and Pierre Trudeau needed in the 1960s and 1980s to forge ahead with smart health laws despite the opposition of some physician associations.

The goal of universal access to primary care is **relevant** for all Canadians. To date, we have a two-tiered system. In this case, I don't mean two tiers as in public-pay systems and private-pay systems. I'm talking about two tiers of access—the haves and the have-nots, the winners and losers. To be precise, the system is actually three-tiered. The luckiest Canadians have access to a full interprofessional primary care team. In Ontario, that's about a quarter of the population. The second tier includes those who have access to a family doctor, but their doctor isn't provided with dedicated funds to hire other health professionals to share the workload and provide additional care such as dietary guidance, counselling, or rehabilitation therapy. The third tier includes the people left out altogether, with no family doctor and no other primary care clinician. It's irresponsible to accept this status quo. It's not as if those Canadians can simply avoid getting sick or figure out for themselves how to screen for cancer and cardiovascular risks. We either pay now or we pay later. But the payment will be more than financial. If we don't fix this current system, the cost will be in lives that are shorter and less healthy than they could be.

The national plan to achieve primary care for all must be **time-bound**. We all know that deadlines work. The trick is to pick a deadline that is both ambitious and achievable, not unlike we did with the Syrian refugees. In the case of ensuring universal access to primary care in Canada, every single day counts, so I'm tempted to err on the side of ambition and propose we do this by 2030. However, that may not be realistic. We need to train more family doctors and primary care NPs, which takes years. Provinces will need to develop their models and strategize about where the new primary care homes need to be established. Budgets and bureaucracies will need to be adjusted to have a greater part of both dedicated to primary care. With all that in mind, I believe we could do this together in the time span of a decade. I suggest our deadline should be the year 2035. That provides enough time to grow the health workforce. It's more than enough time to build the infrastructure. And it's even enough time to ensure that every jurisdiction in the country has elected a government committed to primary care for all. If we have the collective will, we can build the way.

CHAPTER 3

Recovering a Species at Risk

When I was a child, our family doctor was a big, kind man named Dr. Ray Middleton. I can't recall what he actually looked like, but in my memory, it's as if he stepped out of a Norman Rockwell painting, with a white coat, baggy grey trousers, and an ever-ready stethoscope slung around his neck. In the late 1960s, it did not seem unusual that Dr. Middleton would make a house call when my sisters or I were ill. Our family lived in a red-brick Presbyterian manse in Hespeler, Ontario—a house provided by the church where my dad was the minister. I recall one feverish day spent lying on the uncomfortable French provincial chesterfield in the living room, smelling like the Vicks VapoRub that my mother smeared across my chest when I had a respiratory infection. The jovial, trusted Dr. Middleton had arrived to look me over and confidently pronounce a diagnosis. Perhaps he prescribed penicillin for a throat or ear infection. Maybe he simply assured my mother that I would improve with the symptomatic relief she had already offered.

My mother had good reason to be anxious about having a sick child. Just a couple of years earlier, my older brother Gary had acquired influenza when we were living in Winnipeg. In his case, instead of improving with symptomatic treatments, he deteriorated until his condition became critical. He died in Winnipeg General Hospital at the age of six, only three days after he first became sick. I am certain that, with that devastating memory fresh in her mind, my mom appreciated having a family doctor in Hespeler who did house calls and gave informed advice.

Exactly two decades after my brother died, I was a family doctor myself, motivated in part by that experience of childhood grief, and by observing the impact a doctor could have in caring for families. Being a family physician is one of the best jobs in the world. Sadly, not all family doctors would agree with me at this moment in time. Health systems have a workload crisis of proportions beyond the experiences of living memory. The family-physician workforce is feeling the pain of that hit.

While the health workforce writ large was reduced and demoralized by the COVID-19 pandemic, two parts of that workforce have suffered disproportionately. And yet, they are among the very roles we need if we're going to foster and deliver a revolution in primary care. Those two parts are (1) nurses everywhere, and (2) front-line doctors (this includes family doctors, pediatricians, and emergency physicians). It is said you should write about what you know best, so I'm going to focus on the crisis in family medicine—while acknowledging that the nursing shortages are equally worrisome.

As previously described, millions of adults in Canada can't access a family doctor or any other primary care clinician.[1] What's more disturbing is that unless we dramatically change our structures, access to care will get even worse. Over the past decade, year after year, fewer medical school graduates in Canada want to train in the specialty of family medicine. In 2023, it was only 30.3 percent who made it their first choice.[2] More concerning still, in a 2021 survey of Ontario family medicine graduates, only 15 percent were planning to join or start a comprehensive general practice.[3]

A team at the Peterborough, Ontario, site of the Queen's University Family Medicine training program did a study in 2023 to find out where their trainees had gone to practise. Of the recent graduates who were interviewed, only 38 percent are now practising comprehensive family medicine, with the majority of them practising part-time. The deterrents to taking on a full-time comprehensive family practice included: feeling unprepared for the management role; the volume of administrative and non-clinical work; lack of practice opportunities to fit their lifestyle; wanting variety in their career; fear of burnout; seeing preceptors who are burnt out or have unsustainable practices; and the difficulty of taking time off, including parental leave.[4]

Adding to this perfect storm, family doctors are retiring at a rapid rate and the workforce is aging. In Quebec, for example, more than 30 percent of family doctors are over the age of 60.[5]

Family doctors have become a species at risk.

I'm beset with both anxiety and curiosity about this problem. Anxiety because the lack of access to care has brought such urgency to a long-brewing problem that we're sitting on a chance to undertake the most positive restructuring of health care since the 1960s—but we can't do it without family doctors, not to mention all the other clinicians. My curiosity is focused on why family medicine has become a less desirable career choice than it has been in the past.

For me, the best part of being a family doctor is the people—and the incredible privilege of becoming part of the life stories of hundreds of families. My patients and their families have no idea how much they shaped me, almost always in positive ways.

I first met Louise soon after my husband and I, with our children, moved back to Canada from Niger and I had joined a family practice group in Stouffville, Ontario. She showed up at the front desk at the end of a morning clinic, just as the reception staff were ready for a lunch break. I was doing paperwork, and I could hear her animated conversation with a receptionist even though my office was down the hall. "I don't have my fucking health card," she yelled. I knew that was not going to be well-received. I quickly made a beeline to the front desk to prevent the situation from getting worse. Louise had been referred to me by the AIDS Committee of York Region and I was enthusiastic to meet her. I assured my receptionist that we could sort things out about the health card. I suggested she should go have her lunch and it would probably be easiest if I took Louise directly to my office.

That encounter at the front desk was the beginning of what was a more than decade-long relationship with Louise and her family. I came to love them all dearly. Louise had HIV, which had been acquired through injection drug use. I had contacted the AIDS Committee of York Region soon after starting my practice in Stouffville and told them that I was interested in providing primary care to people living with HIV in York Region if they didn't already have a family doctor. Louise was the first of dozens of referrals they sent my way. Once I had taken someone into my practice, it was common to take on family members as well. Eventually, I cared for Louise as well as her ex-boyfriend, her parents, her sister, brother-in-law, niece, and nephew.

I am indebted to Louise and her family for how they trusted me, despite my ignorance about many of the realities of their lives. They were honest, authentic, and appreciative. They didn't hide their complicated stories. I came to grasp why they often missed their appointments and could not comply with every aspect of medical advice. Over time, we grew to understand one another's ways. They made it clear that they needed and valued me. More important, I needed them. They taught me about trauma and discrimination, about living with poverty in York Region, about how hard it is to get access to health and social services if you have no employee benefits, if you have mental illness, if you don't know how to navigate the systems. There was always some kind of drama in their lives. Hearing those stories over the years connected me to them and helped me to see life and its ongoing challenges through their eyes.

It was the people, and especially the complicated family dynamics I was privy to, that made being a family practitioner so rewarding. It's a job that doesn't demonstrate all its joys on a daily basis or even over a short period of time. The rewards are more evident over the long term, and in retrospect. The magic of family medicine accrues over decades. While I've officially been a family doctor since 1986, it was during the seventeen years as a family doctor in the Markham-Stouffville community, when my work life became interwoven with the fabric of countless community members, that the true rewards sank in. This is where I became a better doctor, and a better person.

For exhausted family doctors, who are tempted to walk away from their vocation, these long-standing relationships of caring may become the only thing that keeps them going.

It had been a bit of a culture shock to move to the suburban town of Stouffville, northeast of Toronto, in 1998, after working for a decade in the Sahel region of Niger, West Africa. I had found the community health work in Niger to be tremendously interesting and professionally satisfying, but it wore me out emotionally, and I was ready to move back to Canada.

Pep and I had spent almost our entire married life in Niger, apart from the few trips back home to give birth or to take courses. By the time we returned, it had been twelve years since I finished my family medicine training. I was ready to start a medical practice in Canada.

I knew it would not be hard to find a place to do so. Family doctors have job security. For my entire life, there has never been a time when a family physician could not readily find work in Canada. There is never a shortage of people who seek your services. Most family doctors know it is a huge privilege to have such a job, though that is less often acknowledged in the current context, where the honour is often buried under a heavy blanket of burnout, exhaustion, and resentment.

When we settled in Stouffville, I made a point of meeting with some local doctors to learn about the opportunities. A mutual friend introduced me to Dr. Gwen Sampson, who came to our home for coffee and offered me a job, on the spot, with her group. So, in the fall of 1998, I became part of the Stouffville Medical Centre, a practice established in the 1950s.

It was a delightful small-town practice. I was one of six doctors when I joined. There was a palpable spirit of community service among my colleagues, and it seemed like everyone knew everyone in Stouffville in those days. Between meeting hundreds of patients and their families at work, meeting children and their families in the schoolyard, and meeting people at the church we attended, I quickly got to know the community. I felt embedded and embraced in very short order.

I look back in amazement at some of our practice habits at that time. The doctors took turns covering evenings and weekend clinics, plus being on call. What surprises me, when I think of it now, is that the calls from patients, from the lab, or from nursing homes were routed directly to our home number, our land line, because there were few cell phones at the time. There was no filter. Our home phone numbers were listed in the white pages of the telephone directory. The result was that you would get calls about the wildest things, and at the oddest times, from any patient who wanted to talk to a family doctor—often when you were not on call. Many people assume that doctors are always on work hours, and that we remember every detail of their cases, even when we're out shopping or on the sidelines of a soccer game. Most doctors can tell stories like mine, of how people come up to you in the grocery store aisle to ask about their latest tests for potassium levels or blood counts. Sometimes that was irritating, but for the most part, I found it charming, and often amusing.

It was different in the clinic, though. I embraced the satisfaction and honour of listening to people all day long, knowing that I was providing one of the few places where people could come and unapologetically ask to be cared for. To listen and to care is not a job; it is a privilege.

Family medicine and its appeal have changed a lot since then, and doctors are leaving practice almost as fast as we can train new ones. What has happened to cause these trends? More important, what can we do to reverse them?

These questions are common in the contemporary conversations of family doctors and health system leaders. No one knows all the answers, but there are a range of hypotheses about why we are suddenly struggling to attract and retain family doctors. Below are ten *theories*. I call them theories because some are supported by emerging evidence, while others have not been proven. All are part of the conversations among medical professionals and are worth mentioning here.

1. Our medical school admissions and selection processes may be to blame. There is emerging evidence that some of the current screening steps are biased toward selecting students who will pursue specialties other than family medicine.

2. There is a hidden curriculum in medical schools. Students pick up unintentional messages that family medicine is a less desirable and less respected specialty.

3. It is gender-based discrimination. As more women enter family medicine, the specialty has become feminized, which in turn has made it undervalued.

4. Family medicine can't compete in a world of so many speciality options. Medical students get exposed to at least thirty different areas in

which they could specialize. Family medicine is only one of those options. Maybe it's a miracle that 30 percent still choose this path.

5. Family medicine is too difficult. Students see how hard it is to diagnose undifferentiated conditions or manage complex, chronic diseases. Family doctors must excel at managing uncertainty. Students may prefer to become an expert in a narrower field of practice.

6. It's about the pay gap. In some other specialties, you might earn two or three times as much.

7. It's about the non-stop responsibility and liability. Many new graduates aren't eager to take on a roster of thousands of patients, knowing it's a long-term, year-round commitment.

8. The conditions of work make the specialty unattractive. Many do not want to run a small business. There is a heavy administrative burden that has been exacerbated by the introduction of electronic medical records, the proliferation of forms for insurance and other purposes, and the growing angst of medical-legal risks that increase the requirement for documentation.

9. The introduction of primary care teams has been incomplete. Specialists who practise in a hospital are not expected to do so without the

help of other health professionals, including nurses and many others, paid for by the hospital. Yet most family doctors don't have funding for an interprofessional team to share the workload.

10. It's about public expectations. In urban settings, family doctors feel like glorified gatekeepers for patients who want to be seen by other specialists. This is made worse by fears of liability and litigation if the family doctor doesn't feel confident. The result is the habit of referring cases that should be in the scope of work for family doctors, which has the long-term effect of limiting the breadth of their competence in those domains.

There is some truth to all of these, and it is not an exhaustive list of the possible explanations for the weakened appeal of family medicine. Clearly, the problem is multifactorial, and, as such, the solutions we need must be multi-faceted and comprehensive.

I would like to delve into two broad areas where we could (and should) address several items in the list above and do better at recruiting and retaining family doctors. They are:

- medical education; and
- system-wide reforms, including:
  - improving the conditions of work; and
  - the complete transition to team-based primary care.

The way we train doctors can't solve the whole problem. But there is room for improvement. Medical education hasn't changed much in the last century. The biggest educational innovation in my lifetime was the introduction of problem-based learning when McMaster University launched its medical school in 1965.[6] The founding dean of that school was Dr. John Evans. He and several colleagues rocked the world of medical education—and eventually the world beyond medicine—with small-group learning that was practical, creative, student-centred, and engaging. Rather than having medicine taught to them one body part at a time, or even one body system at a time, students learned through case studies that introduced medical problems in the context of a whole person, in all their medical and social complexity. Students were trained to be self-directed learners.

We are well overdue for another line in the sand, another time of transition to new models of medical education that are focused, in this case, on generalism and the priority of family medicine. I believe we are on the verge of that transition in Canada.

In 2023, with an eye to the future and a new approach, Queen's University launched a satellite campus of our medical school that is dedicated exclusively to the training of family doctors.[7]

Almost all medical schools in Canada are in a growth phase, thanks to increased funding from provinces to support the admission of more students into the Medical Doctor Programs. But we can't keep doing the same thing and expecting different results. At Queen's, we decided to use twenty of those new admission spots to start a campus located in Durham

Region, east of Toronto, in collaboration with hospital partners at Lakeridge Health. The unique features of the program are:

1. An admissions process to recruit students who are committed to family medicine from the start.
2. Teaching done, as much as possible, by family physician–educators.
3. Engagement of community partners in admissions and curriculum development.
4. Early, frequent, and consistent placements in local family medicine clinics.
5. A seamless transition from the MD Program into a family medicine residency, bypassing the resident matching system, with both parts completed over a six-year period.

We have about five thousand applications each year to the Queen's University MD Program. In 2023, for the first time, we invited applicants to submit a supplementary package if they wanted to be considered for the new campus, in addition to our program based in Kingston. For those who submit the supplementary package, a special selection process was designed, in which we attempt to identify applicants who are authentically committed to becoming family doctors. That's never been done before in Canada, and everyone is curious about how effective it will be.

Early feedback is that the admissions process has been labour-intensive for the school—with thousands of file reviews and hundreds of interviews. If we achieve the vision, it will be worth this front-end investment of time. I'm fascinated by the question of how accurately we can identify the traits of a commitment to family medicine even before people start medical school.

This is an innovation provoked by social need. Our education team put the program together under an exceptionally tight timeline. We had our first meetings about the idea in the autumn of 2021. The first students started the program in September 2023. That's lightning speed in the world of universities and governments. We did it that fast because it's that important.

I share here an April 2023 tweet from Dr. Andrew Holt, @CanEMDoc, who wrote: "Blown away by @janephilpott & @QueensUHealth's forward thinking on how to encourage more great family docs. I forsee significant challenges with a dedicated FM med school, & am not convinced it will work as intended but damned if its not worth trying."[8]

He's not the only skeptic, and the program development has had some tensions, disagreements, and logistical bumps along the way. No one in Canada has done this before. We moved quickly, which meant we didn't have time to build the consensus or buy-in that you might ordinarily want for such a significant program change. But even our toughest critics will say that they want us to succeed. Everyone is keen to find new ways to train more great family doctors.

We are often asked how we can force students to stick to their commitment to pursue a family medicine residency and then go into family practice. The answer, of course, is that we can't. After four years, they will get an MD degree, and they could leave the process and apply for a residency in a different specialty. So, the onus is on us, from the start, to demonstrate the importance and the joy of being a family doctor.

We have the opportunity of teaching without the hidden curriculum that biases students away from family medicine. Instead, they should be embedded in a culture that highly values family doctors. Time will reveal how successful we are.

Medical education is certainly part of the solution, but the biggest wins can be found at the level of health systems. We must address the conditions of work for family doctors. Currently, they are overwhelmed with the administrative burden.[9] Filling out paperwork, for example, can be a poor use of their time and skills. Plus, it adds to the risk of burnout. Many family doctors are also frustrated by the inflexibility of the practice arrangements. If you make a commitment to a group of patients, it can be very difficult to take holidays or work part-time. You would be hard-pressed to find a family doctor who doesn't have stories about taking their computer on vacation so they can check lab results and respond to the needs of their patients at least once per day.

Do we really want a family-physician workforce of people who never get a proper holiday?

A Canada with universal access to team-based primary care must include system support so that health professionals can focus on health care and can confidently get a break from their work, knowing that their patients will still receive high-quality care and none of their important results will be missed. The more I think about it, the more I wonder why it's taken us so long to make this happen. Imagine if we trained teachers and then sent them out in the world to open up their own schools, lease the buildings, hire the office staff, and decide how many students they could manage to educate each year. Imagine if we trained surgeons and then asked them to operate without nurses—or radiologists without technicians.

Yet, this is the model that exists for family medicine. Go out and hang up your shingle. Rent and outfit your clinic space. Set up a business. Hire a receptionist. Decide if you should hire a nurse, but know that their salary will come out of your pocket. Find some colleagues to work with, if you like. See if they will cover for you when you want a week off. Or hire a locum doctor (a temporary replacement) to cover for you, also out of your own pocket—if you can find one, that is. Alternatively, if you're sick or out of town, you can shut the doors of your practice and send your patients to the emergency department if they need medical attention, assuming the emergency department is not closed.

If you want autonomy, this is a great gig. But more family doctors are realizing that autonomy comes with a large cost, for both patients and providers. Family doctors of all ages and career stages are voting with their feet and gradually offering a less comprehensive range of services.[10] Some are choosing to focus their practice in one area, like sports medicine or women's health. No doubt they respond to important medical needs in those capacities, but they are no longer generalists. They are not delivering the comprehensive primary care that the population needs and deserves.

We are overdue for a cross-country, system-wide intervention. Politicians, policy-makers, and health care leaders should commit to developing Canada's first national health system that includes a primary care home for everyone.

Think of what we could have: Family doctors will work in teams and use their skills to the top of their scope of competency. Where another clinician on the team can do the same thing just as well, or better, that work should be shared.

The family doctor no longer has to run a small business, unless they choose to be an administrative leader for the team. The team can develop systems to manage messages, lab results, imaging reports, and other follow-up tasks using algorithms with built-in quality improvement, so doctors can sign out when they leave the clinic and know that critical results will not be missed. They can work part-time or take a holiday. There are already a few models like this.[11] But no province yet has pledged to make it universal. It should happen now.

In my current roles—as dean of health sciences at Queen's University, as well as being the CEO of the Southeastern Ontario Academic Medical Organization (SEAMO)—we worked with a range of partners to develop a model for a primary care home intended to respond to all the concerns we've heard from patients and providers about what works.

We call it the Periwinkle Model, a name inspired by the Quintuple Aim—a five-point framework that outlines the goals of high-quality health systems. It is, in turn, an adaptation of the Triple Aim that was first described by Dr. Donald Berwick and his colleagues at the Institute for Healthcare Improvement.[12] The Triple Aim featured the goals of (1) a healthy population, (2) better care, and (3) value for money. Subsequently, the goals of (4) care team well-being and (5) equity were added to the list, thus becoming the widely referenced Quintuple Aim for health care. So as to keep those goals front of mind for our primary care home, we chose the symbol of the periwinkle, a five-petalled flower, and started calling our approach the Periwinkle Model.

The Periwinkle Model is an adaption of the long-established concept of a patient-centred medical home, but with a few variations. It was developed by a list of partners including the local Ontario Health Team and the Kingston Community Health Centre. Queen's University is involved, as is SEAMO. All three local hospitals are champions, along with the City of Kingston and the local public health unit.

The Periwinkle Model is one of many designs of a primary care team for a defined population. The essential ingredient of every primary care home must be a core team of health professionals working collaboratively. It must offer longitudinal care. This is in contrast to a walk-in clinic or an urgent care clinic that does not encourage patients to build a continuous relationship over time. Nor do those sites ordinarily offer preventive care or health promotion. The primary care home is also the best place to keep a patient's long-term electronic health record, which will include community-based visits, public health interventions, hospital visits, lab data, and so much more.

There are a few special features that we want to test in our model that are worth noting. Let's look at them in some detail here.

1. The model is designed for the whole population of a geographic region.

We need to demonstrate a model that would allow primary care to function like public schools. It should be open to everyone who lives in a particular region or postal code who does not already have a family doctor or primary care clinician. (People cannot be assigned to more than one primary care team.) In the fully implemented vision of the Periwinkle Model, you do not curate a selective roster of patients. It's access to care for everyone within a geographic boundary. Because of funding constraints, our first version of the model in Kingston is designed to provide care for ten thousand patients. We hope it can serve as a base module or unit template to be replicated (with modifications) until everyone has a place to get care. The investment to do so for our region would be modest. As with public schools and their coordinating school boards, when the population grows, the health system would add new modules or homes to meet the need.

2. Patients are attached to the whole team.

We know most people would prefer a system where a patient can see the same clinician at every visit.[13] That's simply not possible. The result of pursuing this impossible dream has been a country where patients are divided into haves and have-nots. The Periwinkle Model aims for a balance that recognizes the healing power and importance of interpersonal continuity in person–provider relationships and the reality that no clinician can be available at all times. Every patient will be assigned to a most responsible provider (MRP). The MRP will be a family doctor or NP. This is pragmatically necessary for processes like referrals and hospital records. For non-urgent visits, including periodic health exams or follow-up on chronic diseases, a patient can book with their MRP. But for same-day visits or when the MRP is away, the patient will be triaged and assigned to the most appropriate clinician available. That may be another doctor or NP. It might also be a nurse, a dietician, a social worker, an occupational therapist, a physiotherapist, or a pharmacist, for example. Team members understand and respect each other's roles and competencies. They can often substitute for one another, and in doing so, release everyone to work to the top of their scope of practice. There's more than enough work for all—and no need to compete about which provider is most important. The end result is a system with both continuity and access. It also means that the primary care home can offer services seven days a week and up to twelve hours a day, thereby reducing pressure on emergency departments.

3. Doctors (and others) are paid by salary or by the shift.

Family doctors can be remunerated by a number of methods. Historically, most were paid fee-for-service. Increasingly in Canada, family doctors have been paid according to the size of the roster that they take on. This model has turned out to be somewhat problematic in that not every doctor is available enough to provide access to all the people assigned to them. The result is that millions of Canadians are "unattached," or they are technically "attached" but have unacceptable access.

I was curious about the impact that various payment models have on the job satisfaction of family doctors. In chapter 2, I noted survey results showing a majority of medical school graduates express an interest in working under a salaried model. Is there any evidence that current family doctors paid by salary are more satisfied in their jobs? In a not-yet-published scoping review conducted in 2023 by Queen's University medical students under the guidance of Dr. Colleen Grady, more than thirty studies about physicians' job satisfaction were examined. These publications showed that the fee-for-service model was least associated with satisfaction, often due to the large amount of unpaid administrative work. The levels of satisfaction associated with being salaried were mixed.

Given there is no clear front-runner in payment-model options, and given the possibility that it appeals to new graduates, we decided that in the Periwinkle Model, doctors will be paid by salary, with benefits, if they want to work full-time, as in the Community Health Centre model. There will also be options to work by the shift, with flexible scheduling, not dissimilar to the approach used for many emergency room physicians or intensive care doctors. We understand this is appealing to new graduates.

It should be noted that team-based care will cause the primary care portion of a government's budget to grow, not shrink, if you add therapists, dieticians, and other non-physician workers. These providers can substitute for the work of family doctors where their skillsets overlap. For example, both physicians and dieticians can counsel people with diabetes about what they should eat, but it frees up the doctor's time if the dietician performs this function, and they are probably better trained for it. At other times, team members supplement the work of a doctor by adding skills for which physicians may not be trained. An example of this is the addition of a physiotherapist. In the case of osteoarthritis of the hips or knees, the use of exercise and education programs can reduce pain and improve overall function.[14] Adding a therapist to a primary care team will cost more than a family doctor alone, but it offers better care, plus savings elsewhere if it reduces physical disability and prevents the need for surgery or other interventions. There is strong international evidence that spending more on primary care leads to cost savings in other parts of the system.[15]

4. Accountability is built in.

So, if doctors are not paid fee-for-service, how do we know they will work hard enough for us to get value for public money? This is the fundamental question of value-based health care. Rather than using a transactional system such as fee-for-service, or even a similar system called "shadow-billing," we need to find a way to pay for outcomes rather than output. This is a weakly developed concept in Canada, but there is a lot of interest in figuring it out. One of the promising areas of work is the use of patient feedback as an accountability tool. Some clinics use patient-reported experience metrics and patient-reported outcome metrics to demonstrate accountability. The experience metric is like the text message or email you get from a retail or hospitality provider asking you to rate your encounter. Based on this feedback, the learning health system can be incentivized for improving the quality of the care experience. There are many outcome metrics that can also be used. For example, how many times was a visit to the emergency department averted because the primary care home offered good access to care? What proportion of newborns in the community are attached to primary care by six weeks of age? Once metrics such as these are standardized and publicized across all regions, there will be many opportunities for learning from one another.

Ideally, accountability should go both ways. Family doctors in capitated models are expected to be accountable and available to the patients they have accepted on their rosters. Emergency rooms are left to deal with the overflow if there is insufficient access to care. But there is no system-level accountability from governments to establish enough primary care services in a region so that each clinician will have a manageable workload. In a growing urban population, we would never expect schools to keep taking more students in each classroom and blame them for lacking accountability if they didn't. There are well-developed public processes to determine when schools need to be opened or closed, boundaries changed, classrooms added, or facilities upgraded. The organization of primary care could mimic these structures.

In Norway, where the municipality is responsible for providing doctors and guaranteeing access to care, an increase in population is met with a recruitment of family doctors. Each municipality understands their local needs, coordinates this recruitment, and works to meet the guarantee that each resident has a doctor. If clinic space is limited, the municipality may ask a group practice to move to a larger space that can accommodate more doctors, allowing expansion of their services, or they can support incoming family doctors to establish a new clinic in a high-need area.

5. The workforce is expanded through learners and volunteers.

I have learned many things as dean of health sciences at Queen's University. We have a School of Medicine, a School of Nursing, and a School of Rehabilitation Therapy. Currently, we are undergoing expansion in all our schools, but especially in medicine and nursing. There are several barriers limiting our ability to expand. One frustrating example is the limited availability of clinical placements for learners. We could train more health professionals if we could find more places for them to get practical experience. Yes, it adds to your workload when you have a student in the workplace, but it can also add to your work satisfaction, and sometimes, it means more work can get done. One of our core values in the Periwinkle Model for primary care is to be learner friendly. This means that both team members and patients welcome the presence of medical students, nursing students, occupational therapy and physical therapy students, family medicine residents, and others. In the orientation process, we will inform patients that a student (under supervision) will be involved in most visits. This has many benefits. Learners can learn. And learners can help, by documenting the details of the visit, assisting with follow-up plans, and responding to questions from patients. In my experience, most patients are happy to see learners, and some positively love the chance to meet young people. Learners and patients need one another, and the system is the winner when this dynamic is built into the standard of care. Similarly, primary care can offer more volunteer placements for people of all ages who are keen to find useful and meaningful roles.

6. Services are expanded through the use of community partners.

The ideal primary care home can be the hub of a range of health and social services. In fact, it's the natural home base for palliative care, home care, and mental health care. If possible, it includes community paramedics who can be an extension of the care team into the homes of patients. Under the best-case scenario, it is a one-stop shop where patients can get their primary care needs met and conveniently access other services such as laboratory testing, imaging, and filling prescriptions. To take it a step further, we envision the future of the Periwinkle Model to be a site for additional services such as legal aid, housing, and volunteer tax clinics.

There is more I could say about how to restructure and fortify the clinical foundations of health and well-being. But too many suggestions can overwhelm us, and nothing gets done. Decades' worth of reports on health care, with hundreds of recommendations, have left us with little more than superb policy documents. We need to focus our attention on one big thing. If we could pick one grand national project that would have the greatest impact on health care, it would be the construction of a robust system for universal access to primary care.

PART TWO

Spiritual

CHAPTER 4

Hope

Health is determined by more than social structures, politics, and clinical care systems, the latter of which we explored in the previous section. The health of each person's soul or spirit should not be ignored in the considerations of what it takes to be a healthy society. A person can be healthy in their physical body and have their material needs met, but they are not truly well if they are suffering on the inside. We could be a country with functioning health systems, support for the social determinants of health, and a nurturing political context. In that utopia, it's possible that many people would still not be well. We must also ponder the determinants of personal wellness, including mental and spiritual health—subjects that are not often included in books of this nature, nor in the conversations we are having about health care and the national challenges we face.

Health professionals might find it more comfortable talking about mental wellness than spiritual wellness. That's fair. But let's remember that mental health is more than the absence of mental illness. The World Health Organization defines overall health as "a state of complete physical, mental and social well-being and not merely the absence of disease and infirmity."[1] We could adapt that to say that mental health is a complete state of emotional, psychological, and spiritual well-being, not merely the absence of psychiatric illness. Without mental wellness, it's hard to focus on the rest of one's well-being. As the adage goes, there is no health without mental health.

In 1979, I moved an hour's drive west of our family home in Hespeler to attend the University of Western Ontario in London. On the northwest side of Western's campus, there is a large student residence that is officially called Saugeen-Maitland Hall, and unofficially known as the Zoo. At the time, it was understood to be the place for the best parties, the least studying, and the most mediocre food. I understand the food has improved considerably, but despite the best efforts of the university administration to change the narrative, the residence has retained the nickname and its reputation as party central.

When my parents dropped off their eighteen-year-old daughter at the Zoo, at the start of frosh week, with her most precious belongings jammed into two cardboard boxes, they had some trepidation. We drove up to the doors of the residence and our family car was swarmed by enthusiastic sophomores, which did not exactly calm my parents' fears. My dad couldn't hide his anxiety about whether this was a safe place to release me. Would I be swept up in the wild and reckless freedom that was suddenly an option, or would I hunker down and soak up the opportunity to study at this distinguished institution, the same university he had attended? He needn't have worried. With only a bit of temptation to do otherwise, I chose the latter and focused on my studies, enough to get me early acceptance into medical school at Western. It would also turn out to be the place where I began to take my Christian faith seriously.

I had grown up under the influence of parents and grandparents who were all part of the Presbyterian branch of Protestantism. My dad was a minister, and our whole family attended church not just on Sundays but also through church-related activities and programs almost every day of the week. It was our social circle and our predominant culture.

As a child, I don't remember questioning whether to believe what we were taught at church. It was our assumed identity. The focus of our faith was on service. As the model of servanthood, we learned about the life of Jesus Christ. The Bible teaches that he is the Son of God, which was never a stretch for me to accept. I knew my dad spent many hours preparing beautiful sermons for each Sunday morning, conveying messages that were easy to understand and highly pragmatic. I don't recall much emphasis on the afterlife; it was about how to be useful in the here and now. Nor do I remember anyone in our denomination talking about whether or not you were "saved." Dad's sermons were about following the example of Jesus by real-world service to humankind.

It was at university that I met people who blew open the doors of my mind on the topic of faith. They were charismatic. They talked about their faith in an intimate way I had never experienced before. As I listened, I felt an urgency to take my faith more seriously. Many of these friends had a story about a personal decision to become a Christian. For them, faith was more than their hereditary culture. This concept fascinated me, even though I could not point to a specific conversion experience of my own. The closest I came to the phenomenon was while attending a rather wild party at the Zoo, the kind that seemed to occur almost nightly. It was easy to imagine a future life at university with self-indulgence as the key focus. I left the party early and went back to my dorm room, and that evening I made a conscious decision not to follow the partying path. I wanted to explore spiritual life more fully. I sat on my bed, picked up my Bible, and started to read it with an open, curious mind.

What I found in that book was something and someone to believe in. Some parts didn't make sense, and they still don't. But the chapters that described the words and actions of Jesus, and what we could learn from him, were full of practical teaching. They showed me a way to live.

I particularly love the parts of the Bible written by the apostle Paul. In addition to my university studies, I memorized large chunks of the ancient letters he wrote. Those words are still embedded in my psyche to draw upon, to check myself and see if I'm living accordingly. The formative values I found in those words have stuck with me and guided my work in medicine and public service. They include admonitions like this from a letter Paul wrote to the Philippians: "Do nothing out of self-ish ambition or vain conceit. Rather, in humility value others above yourselves, not looking to your own interests but each of you to the interests of the others."[2]

Christian faith has always been a part of my life, but from my university days onward, it was because I chose to believe and not simply because it was my heritage. What I didn't real-ize then, and only understand in retrospect, is that faith has given me resilience. The choice to believe in something and someone beyond the material world has been a key to mental wellness for me. It gave me hope. On the worst days of my life, I had something and someone to believe in.

The concept of believing in something divine or someone bigger than yourself, or more enduring than yourself, should be recognized as a key to fortitude. For millennia, in cultures around the world, people have endured hardships of all manner, strengthened by belief in a higher power or a larger purpose. In modern Western cultures, secular humanism has become the default faith. Humanism may not involve the supernatural, but I still consider it a type of faith—the hope, in this case, is in humanity, including the human abilities of reason and science.

My point, for the purpose of this book, is that spiritual resources such as faith and hope offer value for personal wellness. If this book is to consider the well-being of a country, that should include guidance about how to support the wholeness of its people. I offer a framework for this—and it starts with hope as a core ingredient for wellness.

Hope is about the future. It is the expectation that good things await. Hope is a patient and optimistic anticipation about the days to come. Hope is essential for whole-person health, and collective hope enhances the well-being of society. Hope is an essential element at the centre of mental wellness. To be healthy, we need hope circulating through our minds— as much as we need blood streaming through our arteries and veins, as much as we need oxygen flowing into the depths of our lungs. Hope sustains us. Hope is what helps each of us face another day. It is at the start of every project you undertake and every relationship you start.

To lose hope, to be without hope, is a dangerous state of being. It puts a person or a society at high risk of harm. The preservation or restoration of hope for individuals, communities, and society is core business for the well-being of a country. If we're going to be a country with health for all, that needs to include the wholeness of each person, outside and inside.

As minister of health, I was fortunate to be introduced to the First Nations Mental Wellness Continuum (FNMWC) Framework.[3] When it was first described to me, it was one of those rare moments when a thousand contemplations were suddenly crystalized with clarity and awe.

The FNMWC Framework was developed in an iterative process under the guidance of Dr. Carol Hopkins, CEO of the Thunderbird Partnership Foundation.[4] It required years of ceremony and discernment. It was informed by hundreds of people—First Nations leaders, youth, community members, and Elders—and was supported by the First Nations and Inuit Health Branch of the federal government, as well as the Assembly of First Nations. It's a brilliant piece of work.

The concepts of the FNMWC are illustrated with the shape of a circle in an attractive multicoloured graphic emerging from a warm, terra cotta background.[5] The key themes form the outer edges of the circle, starting with culture as the foundation. As you move toward the centre of the circle, you find dozens of interconnected elements that are essential for wellness. You'll see some that you've never thought about before in the context of health, and others that will make you nod your head in agreement. Eventually you reach the centre, the heart of mental wellness, where there are four core elements: hope, belonging, meaning, and purpose.

When I came to that part of the graphic for the first time, it was as if a light turned on inside my brain. "Yes, that's it," I said to everyone in the room. "That's what makes us well." I love this framework. I use it as a reminder of my personal need for hope, belonging, meaning, and purpose, in order to be well.

I asked Dr. Hopkins for her blessing to share the framework in this book. She was delighted that more people would learn about the FNMWC and believed some would find healing through its teachings. Still, I felt anxious about whether it was okay for a non-Indigenous person to take a framework, developed by First Nations for First Nations, and use it not only to examine my own life but to suggest that others consider using it. So, I reached out to Dr. Christopher Mushquash as well. I first met Dr. Mushquash at a health conference hosted by Nishnawbe Aski Nation at a beautiful setting in Thunder Bay, on the shores of Lake Superior. Dr. Mushquash is Ojibway. He is a clinical psychologist and an expert in the study of Indigenous mental health and addiction.

I asked him not only if it was okay to point non-Indigenous people in the direction of the FNMWC, but also whether I was at risk of misinterpreting it. What if I used it wrong? I wasn't involved in building the framework, and I don't have the cultural background to understand it all. His response was helpful. He reminded me there are many therapeutic practices that have their roots in Indigenous ways but can be helpful for the healing and blessing of anyone. Dr. Mushquash also eased my mind about potential mistakes. He compared the teachings of the FNMWC to other Indigenous healing practices such as smudging or getting out on the land. In his view, you ought not to be overly prescriptive about the exact way to follow such practices. They are restorative. They have been understood and used by Indigenous Peoples for millennia. They may be shared.

With that foundation, I share this framework as a tool to understand the roots of spiritual wellness. It seems too crass to think of it as a recipe or a checklist—but here's another analogy. To be physically well, we all know that you have to have nutritious food, some exercise, and regular checkups with your health care team. We also understand the social factors that are widely understood as determinants of health, including housing, education, and income. But until I came across the FNMWC Framework, I never had a list of factors to help me understand the underpinnings of spiritual wellness. I hope others find the framework as helpful as I have for understanding the elements that I might be missing or what I need to hang on to.

When I was minister of health, Indigenous leaders were quick to remind me that good health requires much more than clinical service delivery. This lesson was clear when our government was hastily trying to respond to a youth suicide crisis in an isolated First Nations community. The knee-jerk response of government had generally been to come up with a quick fix—to send in mental health workers or to establish a crisis hotline. These superficial solutions at the level of service delivery could help with only part of the problem. A deeper response was needed to account for all the other determinants of health. This included support for the social needs of communities, such as education, housing, and clean water. This also included support for the personal roots of wellness—for young people to have hope, belonging, meaning, and purpose, all linked to their culture.

If hope is so important to mental wellness, from what resource is it derived? How can hope be created where it does not naturally emerge or exist? What gives a person reason for optimism, reason to believe that something positive will happen? What gives you the confidence to look forward? There may be many answers. Some might base their hope on knowledge of the past, some on science and rational thinking. Others have a personality that is more naturally hopeful—though that could be based on past experiences or environments.

I asked Dr. Hopkins about hope, and where it comes from. In her wisdom, based on hundreds of conversations with First Nations people, she explains that hope is rooted in beliefs and values. It is connected to faith. "You have to go beyond the physical realm," she said. "It is about a relationship with the spirit of creation. Hope is more than rational knowledge. It is intuitive knowledge."

This rang true to me. Hope is more than a scientific calculation of what's likely to happen. The hope that offers wellness comes from the soul, where not everything can be measured.

We should be able to agree that hope is essential to whole-person health, and yet, there could be multiple sources of hope. I've described one of the most common birthplaces of hope—a belief that goes beyond the material world, a belief in a higher power, an acceptance of a spiritual realm, perhaps the belief in a creator, a faith in Yahweh, Allah, God.

None other than Nancy Pelosi, speaker emerita of the United States House of Representatives, described it this way: "When people ask me, 'Where is hope? Why shouldn't we give up?' I'll say, hope is where it has always been, sitting comfortably between faith and charity. People have faith in the goodness of others. That gives them hope. So, faith was key to all of it."[6]

Hope and faith are unavoidably linked. I've concluded that if we are going to sustain hope for ourselves as individuals, as well as for ourselves as a society, we need to talk about what we believe. This is not to say that each person needs to embrace a religious faith. My point is that in our pluralist culture, we need to find a positive, public, non-judgmental space for conversations about our convictions.

Canada prides itself on its diversity. We are a rich mosaic of Indigenous Peoples, settlers, and the descendants of settlers. More than 90 percent of us trace our ancestral roots to another part of the world. From those other parts of the world, we brought a panoply of cultures, ethnicities, and faith traditions. Before the settlers came, Indigenous people already had a rich diversity of cultures, languages, and beliefs. We have good reason to be proud of our multicultural society.

In spite of that—in dominant Canadian culture—it has been a widely established maxim of etiquette that the topic of beliefs is to be avoided in polite conversation. Maybe it's time to change that. Maybe the best way to promote peace and harmony in a multi-faith society, and to demonstrate freedom of religion, is to create the conditions where it is safe and acceptable to admit, unashamedly, in the public square, that you are a person of faith, if you are.

Until now, I have rarely spoken publicly about my faith. But without doubt, it's been a source of hope for me, and thereby a source of wellness. Therefore, if I care about the wellness of the people around me, I should not be afraid to share the story of my faith. Maybe it will help someone else find hope through accepting the existence of a higher power.

It has been a protective buffer, introducing peace, patience, and perspective for the trials of life. This is not unique to a particular religion. Belief in a spiritual world means, by definition, that earthly tribulations are both more bearable and more fathomable. For people who do not believe in a higher power, I imagine that kind of assurance about something you can't prove might sound ridiculous. But in my experience, I have found faith to be a reliable grounding.

Some will argue that religious faith is a false sense of security. I don't expect everyone to believe what the Bible says, and if someone doesn't believe it to be authoritative, we should place no expectations on them to follow its teachings. But I happen to believe it. It's got some unusual and even disturbing parts, to be sure, but overall, it makes sense. It gives me an understanding that I have received grace, and now I have an obligation to use that blessing and pass it on. From the time I decided with conviction to believe in a creator, whom I call God, my faith has been a source of peace, stability, and direction.

Hope, regardless of its source, is an essential ingredient for mental wellness. Faith in a spiritual world, or a higher power, is a legitimate source of hope, which in turn supports mental wellness. None of us should be ashamed to admit out loud that we are people of faith. It is not incompatible with the acceptance of science, data, history, paleontology, or archeology.

We must also have the freedom to worship the higher power of our choice—and respect the choices of others. All the major religions, including the spiritual teachings of Indigenous Peoples, have core values in common: truth, justice, compassion, peace, humility, care for creation, and more. An open discourse grounded in these commonly held values is not something to be suppressed. It is an opportunity to promote the wellness of both individuals and society.

CHAPTER 5

Belonging

My first real understanding of the concept of belonging came around a crowded little table in Hespeler, Ontario. Except for Sundays, when we used the dining room, all six members of my family ate supper at a round, pine kitchen table held up by a thick central pedestal.

One evening, the conversation revolved around the news of a teenager in our town who was pregnant. Soon to be a teenager myself, I paid close attention to the narrative, though I now have no recollection of the girl's name. Perhaps I never knew. My mom said that the girl's family had "disowned" her. I wondered what that meant and imagined something awful. Our parents made it abundantly clear to me and my three sisters that, ideally, we wouldn't become pregnant as teenagers. But their key message was this: "No matter what the future holds, there is nothing you could do in your whole life that would ever separate us from you." In other words, we would never be "disowned." Our parents would never stop loving us. Their commitment to us had no conditions attached.

Mom and Dad didn't just speak those words; they meant them, and acted consistently in that regard. Whatever emotional stability I have in my life, that memory offers the recipe for how my parents created it. There was never a doubt. They would love me, no matter what. That discourse and others like it taught me to accept myself and any circumstances that come my way, knowing that there are relationships on which I can depend. The effect of the conversation was not only that I felt loved, but also that I knew I was worthy of being loved, not because of anything I had done, but because my parents had the capacity to love without strings attached. In doing so, they offered a foundational layer of emotional titanium, a coating to envelop and protect me from the inevitable troubles that one should expect through life. It's an extraordinary gift to be loved exactly as you are. It teaches you to love yourself and others that way as well. That layer of mental resilience comes from belonging. I belong with my family. I am loved as I am.

There was nuance inside the message of unconditional love from our parents. Nothing would make them stop loving us; that was a given. But there was another assumption: from those to whom much is given, much is expected. We were fortunate to be raised in a place of peace, stability, and security; to receive a high-quality, publicly funded education; to have our physical needs met. We were recipients of unmerited favour. It was to be used for good, to make the world more just. Mom and Dad taught us that what you are given is not simply the social and material assets that put you in a position of privilege, and therefore responsibility. What you are given may also be pain or suffering. To receive those experiences also confers an obligation that your survival of the difficulty could and should be used to benefit others. Many years later, I would be put to the test of how to use the lessons that grief would bestow upon me.

The result of all that grounding from our parents was attachment—a stable cultural identity and the confidence to know we have a place to belong. And that there are people to whom we belong.

Belonging means connectedness. It is about knowing who you are. It offers the security to be who you are. Belonging is the assurance of a place or a people to which or to whom you can always return. It is the shelter in the storm. It is the open arms of the parent who arranges a feast to welcome back the prodigal child, even if they've done nothing to deserve it. Belonging is recognized in the FNMWC Framework as a core element at the centre of mental wellness.

In contrast, the absence of belonging is well known to be a driver of ill health for individuals. In childhood and adolescence, this may manifest itself in a range of conditions, including substance use disorders or psychiatric illnesses sometimes caused by a lack of attachment.[1] In adulthood, the lack of belonging may show up simply as loneliness—one of the most widespread public health problems of our times.[2]

At the societal level, Canada's history is scarred with a disastrous demonstration of what happens when hundreds of thousands of children are deprived of their sense of belonging because they are forcibly removed from their families—their land, their language, their lineage, and their loved ones. This was the result of the Indian residential schools policies and practices that go back to the founding of our country and whose echoes were continued in the Sixties Scoop as well as the current and ongoing "Twenty-First-Century Scoop"—that is, the current overrepresentation in our child welfare systems of children who are Indigenous or otherwise racialized. I will discuss both the tragedy and various solutions related to Indigenous child welfare in chapter 10.

If belonging is so important to mental wellness, it's worthwhile to consider what we can do to promote it or to enhance it. Belonging is linked to a number of other factors that are known to enhance mental wellness:

- the presence of a secure, personal, cultural identity;
- acceptance—the assurance of being loved in your authentic identity; and
- having a social network—not the online kind, the in-real-life kind.

In an ideal scenario, the roots of belonging start even before birth and are positively impacted by the conditions of your infancy and childhood. I would argue that the greatest gift you can give to a child is a sense of belonging. Most parents want to see their children grow up to be happy and healthy. Parents with material affluence may be quick to ensure their children have all the assets and opportunities money can buy. Meanwhile, the best thing parents can bestow on their children cannot be bought with silver or gold. It is unconditional love, and in fact, it's priceless. I say this with confidence because it's the best gift I ever received.

I describe the receipt of that gift with some hesitation because I recognize my profound unearned privilege. The lottery of birth is not fair. I am one of the beneficiaries of a system where some people are born to an environment of safety and support, while others enter a world of danger, uncertainty, or constant struggle. I would be a different person if I hadn't been born into the home of Wallace and Audrey Little. I hit the jackpot.

Being the recipient of unconditional love and having a family or community where you belong is a powerful protective force for mental wellness. If we can offer that to others, we must. But what if you didn't grow up with parents like Wallace and Audrey Little? What if you were loved with conditions, with strings attached? In that case, it may be harder to find belonging, but it should never be impossible. Here are a few ideas that might help:

- **Choose wisely.** You can't choose the family you were born with. But often you can choose the people you spend time with. There are many reasons why we become friends or acquaintances with the people we do, and why we stick with them. At times, our motives are not always healthy. Do yourself a favour and stick with the friends who care about you as you are, without strings attached.

- **Know yourself.** Be yourself. Love yourself. If you don't know about your heritage, this might be the time to start learning. Study your culture and its history. Own your identity with pride and dignity. If you already have a healthy sense of belonging and connection, then be who you are, authentically and unapologetically. Most of all, believe you are precious. You are worthy of love.

• **Become a volunteer.** You may have to get creative, but there are a surprising number of places where you might find belonging as a volunteer. For example, I was amazed at the community we built in a short time among the volunteers who helped on my political campaigns. Many are still connected and have become friends. If politics isn't your interest, think about what is, and look for opportunities to volunteer your time and talent in that field.

• **Love others unconditionally.** There's an ancient prayer attributed to St. Francis of Assisi that includes these words: "Let me not seek as much to be consoled as to console; to be understood as to understand; to be loved as to love." Those are wise words, and helpful guidance for some serious self-reflection. I would argue that especially within families, especially with our children, our love and acceptance of others ought to be unconditional. It often, though not always, has a way of bouncing back in the same form.

- **Seek counselling.** I am not a therapist.
  These ideas come from what I've learned
  as a family doctor and a family member.
  If you're struggling with self-acceptance and
  a sense that you don't belong anywhere,
  please consider seeking professional help.
  This could mean telephone help such as
  the new Canada-wide crisis hotline (988),
  or longer-term counselling with a therapist.
  You deserve to know that you are loved and
  loveable. You deserve to be connected to
  good people.

Beyond what we can do as individuals to promote belonging, this is an important matter for communities and society. Humans are hard-wired to need a social network. Despite the fact that there are now countless ways for people to find an online virtual social network, almost everyone needs at least a small network—like a family or a community—in real life. This has an impact on wellness and productivity in the workplace, and it deserves to be prioritized in both public health and public policy. It turns out that when people don't have a place to belong or people to whom they feel connected, it can harm the well-being of individuals and groups.

The absence of belonging has been proven to be detrimental to your health. This is highlighted by the newly recognized public health crisis of widespread loneliness. In May 2023, US surgeon general Vivek Murthy released an eighty-five-page advisory about the epidemic of loneliness and the health benefits of social belonging and community.[3] It's an impressive piece of work that calls for a national strategy to advance social connection. One prominent chart in the document shows that the lack of social relationships may be as dangerous as smoking fifteen cigarettes per day. People who are lonely have higher rates of heart disease and are at a higher risk for strokes.

That advisory has amplified the spotlight on this problem, but the signs of concern have been known for some time. As a result, the United Kingdom government has had a minister for loneliness since 2018. At least one other country, Japan, has done the same. Some health care organizations and corporations in the United States have appointed a "chief togetherness officer."

We have some catch-up work to do on this in Canada. But imagine how well this could fit in with the vision of the primary care home I described in part one. Each primary care home could identify a leader for togetherness, and the venue itself could be a place for people to come together in groups not only for health care or teaching sessions but with an explicit goal of building social connection. This idea may benefit from the growing interest among health care professionals in the concept of social prescribing—that is, connecting patients to non-clinical services in the community.

We already have excellent models to draw from. Kingston, Ontario, is the birthplace of a project called Oasis Senior Supportive Living, a superb example of how to promote belonging and, in doing so, improve mental wellness. It started when the Frontenac-Kingston Council on Aging, led at the time by Christine McMillan, worked with older adults who were tenants in the same apartment building. Together, they planned a series of social events including meals, crafts, and exercise,

supported by an onsite coordinator who helped tenants facilitate the activities. A phenomenon was born. My colleagues at
Queen's University—Dr. Catherine Donnelly and Dr. Vincent
DePaul—learned about it when one of their students wrote a
paper describing the program. They immediately recognized
its potential and collaborated with the group's founders to
spread the concept to communities across the country.

Oasis is a modest, affordable solution in response to the
problem of loneliness in older adults. It takes advantage of
the fact that many seniors find themselves living in NORCs
(naturally occurring retirement communities): apartment
buildings or neighbourhoods that are not specifically designed
for, but happen to be home to, higher proportions of older
adults. But despite being surrounded by people of their own
age group and stage of life, with plenty of available leisure
time, many are lonely and socially isolated, which puts their
health at risk. They may need a simple nudge to find one
another and make connections.

The Oasis solution is a way of bringing those people together, in a shared space, with the three key goals of promoting
(1) socialization, (2) physical activity, and (3) healthy nutrition.

Drs. Donnelly and DePaul have been studying the effects
of building social connections in this way, and they've already
demonstrated the impressive result that participation in the
Oasis program can delay the need for adults to move into a
long-term care facility by a year or more.[4] I strongly recom-
mend watching Dr. Donnelly describe it beautifully in an
online research talk,[5] if you want to learn more.

CHAPTER 6

Meaning

We were driving on a quiet highway that runs along the southern edge of the Sahara Desert on the day that our daughter Emily died. It happened about an hour west of the city of Maradi. It was the worst day of my life. It was also the day that set the course for the rest of my life's work.

To understand how it happened, I need to provide a bit of history. Maradi was one of three places where our family lived in Niger, West Africa, over the nine years we called that country home. Niger was colonized by the French starting in the late nineteenth century. It regained independence in 1960, but French is still one of eleven official languages. French is used in business, government, and media. But across most of south-central Niger, Hausa is the trade language. It is the mother tongue, the language of the heart. Most of our work was in Galmi, where few women spoke French at the time. If I was going to make friends and work in the hospital, I needed to learn the language. I admire the lexicon and can still converse in it, on the infrequent occasion that I run into another Hausa-language speaker in Canada.

I had a tutor for Hausa, but our colleagues suggested it would be helpful to get away from the hospital environment to focus on language study, and the mission ran a Hausa training program in Maradi. So, in January 1991, we packed up our family with a plan to spend six months living at a mission compound in the southwest end of Maradi, for intensive Hausa study. We looked forward to life in the city.

At the time, we had two daughters. Emily was two and a half. Bethany was a baby. Pep and I both wanted to study Hausa full-time, so we hired a kind and matronly caregiver named Salamatou to care for the girls while we took classes. Bethany enjoyed much of her days being strapped onto Salamatou's back with a colourful zeni cloth, in the classic Hausa tradition. Emily was a quiet toddler, content to explore the compound outdoors or to sit inside, looking at books or making pictures. We had a happy routine.

We'll never know for certain where or when the dangerous bacteria entered the bloodstream of our daughters, but I have always believed it happened on a Saturday stroll in the nearby village of Soura. It was mid-March, toward the end of the harmattan season in the Sahel, a time infamous for the dusty winds that blow in from the Sahara, carrying with them the sandy brown particles that fill the air, sometimes so thick it obstructs visibility, not unlike a snowstorm. At this point in each calendar year, it has been months since there has been a drop of rain. The air is hot and dry. The ground is thirsty. It will still be a couple of months yet before the rains begin again.

The harmattan winds were strong that afternoon. After lunch, we went walking with our friends and our two young daughters. Emily was old enough to run in the sand with the other children. Bethany was a babe in arms. On a hillside at the edge of the village, we watched as the wind stirred up dust and sand. In the snapshot of my memory, everyone is smiling in amazement at the power of the wind, but also not finding it terribly pleasant as the blowing sand filled our eyes and nostrils with grit.

The outbreaks of meningococcal infection that occur across the Sahel from February to April are linked to these dry harmattan winds. In addition to the airborne nature of transmission, there is scientific evidence that the wind and sand particles directly damage the membranes of the throat and lungs, making them more susceptible to the bacteria's entry into the bloodstream.[1] None of that was on our minds at the time of our pleasant visit to the village.

Our schedule on the Sunday of that weekend was also full. We attended a local church in the morning, as was our routine. On Sunday afternoon we drove across town to relax at the historic French Club. The venue was the closest we could get to paradise. The facilities had become run down, but there was a large, concrete swimming pool we loved, and the best treat of all was that you could order soft drinks and fries to be delivered poolside.

I remember well that Sunday at the pool in Maradi. Our last full day with Emily was a happy one. She wore bright orange water wings, and jumped into that pool with the great delight that toddlers discover when they lunge into the air and learn the pleasure of landing in cool, refreshing waters. She wanted to jump off the edge over and over again. Pep and I took turns sitting on the white metal lounge chairs in the shade with Bethany, while the other one took in the joy of splashing about with Emily in the shallow end of the pool. It was a glorious afternoon.

The next morning, we were awakened by the sound of Emily vomiting. We went in to check and discovered she also had a fever. That made me anxious. My worry was the risk of malaria, a common cause of childhood fever in Niger. Of course, we took anti-malaria pills as prophylaxis. In those days, the recommended regimen was daily proguanil and weekly chloroquine—which tastes awful. It was a weekly challenge to get the children to swallow those bitter tablets, crushed inside jam or chocolate spread to make them more tolerable.

A case of chloroquine-resistant malaria was always a possibility and a fear. So, we decided we should get Emily tested. We packed up both daughters and headed to the lab. As we drove, I had a fleeting thought about how my parents must have felt heading to the hospital when my older brother, Gary, died. I considered afterward that this must have been one of the ways that God was preparing me for the worst outcome. Although Emily didn't seem all that sick, the possibility of life-threatening illness had been inserted into my head.

The malaria smear was negative, and her white blood count was normal. She had no signs or symptoms of illness other than the fever and vomiting, so it seemed most likely that she had some kind of virus, and we should treat the symptoms with acetaminophen and rest.

Both girls had received routine vaccines. Because we lived in Niger, this included Menomune, an old, now discontinued vaccine against meningococcus. Menomune never had the efficacy of the new conjugate meningitis vaccines, and its protective effect for children was even less, but the girls had been vaccinated and that was at least some reassurance that meningococcal disease should have been quite unlikely.

I stayed home from Hausa class that morning. Emily rested in our bed. It is with heartache that I recall working in the kitchen while she slept. Almost all our breads and pastries were homemade, except for the baguettes you could buy on the street corners. So, it was not unusual for me to be baking. But I remember it because it's one of the things I felt guilty about in retrospect. Knowing now that these were Emily's last hours with us, I struggle to forgive myself for not spending every minute by her side. How could I have spent those precious hours doing something so mundane as baking bread? How did I not understand she was dying?

Pausing my work, I went into the bedroom to check her again. That's when I saw the telltale rash—a clear indication of meningococcemia. I knew immediately what we were facing, and felt my heart sink in my chest with a thud.

The rash of meningococcemia is the most frightful I have ever seen. It is a dark, horrifying purple. It is unmistakable. It means that the *Neisseria meningitidis* bacteria, which is best known for infecting the spinal cord and other parts of the nervous system, has instead entered directly into the bloodstream and is circulating throughout the body. The rash is caused when tiny blood vessels burst and little pools of blood accumulate under the skin.

Meningococcemia is a rapidly progressive, highly fatal infectious disease. The instant I saw that rash, I knew we were up against an unrelenting clock. Emily had to get injectable penicillin as soon as possible. Pep and I quickly put both girls in the car and headed for a place where we knew we would get good care. It would be a two-hour drive to the mission hospital located in Galmi. I've since wondered why we didn't consider looking for a clinic in Maradi. As I face the facts now, I know nothing would have saved Emily at that point—and it later turned out that for Bethany's sake it was a good thing we headed to Galmi Hospital—but I can't recall our thought processes about deciding where to go. I'm not even sure we discussed it. We just headed to a place where we knew we would find love, support, and high-quality medical care.

We set out on the road in our white Mitsubishi Lancer. Pep drove. Bethany was in her infant car seat beside him. I was in the back beside Emily. I don't think we have ever driven so quickly. I don't recall talking much. We were praying silently.

We were about an hour into our trip, just past the village of Guidan Roumdji, when dear little Emily suddenly had a seizure. Not a long, awful one, but it was definitely a seizure. Just as I was panicking and wondering what I could do, the seizure movements stopped. Everything stopped. She had stopped breathing.

That was the time and place our daughter Emily died. But we couldn't say it out loud then. We couldn't admit it to ourselves. We couldn't accept we were living a parent's worst nightmare. We were on a highway halfway to our destination. How could we stop and face the truth?

I told Pep that she had stopped breathing and we had to do CPR to keep her alive. I held her body across my lap and tried to breathe life back into her, crying and breathing and praying all at the same time. We had more than an hour to go. I became exhausted, so Pep and I changed places. He held his precious girl in the back seat and kept going with CPR. We couldn't let ourselves stop believing we might be able to keep her alive. I drove, literally with the pedal to the metal.

As I drove, I sang in prayers, pleading for God's grace, crying out for a miracle. This was decades before cell phones were available, so we had no way to let our colleagues at Galmi Hospital know that we were getting close, or what had happened along the way. It turns out they knew we were coming. Our colleagues in Maradi had found a way to call ahead to say we were heading in that direction.

They did not know that Emily had died during the trip. Nor did anyone know that Bethany had developed the same frightful purple rash of meningococcemia. This cruel infection had taken the life of our firstborn child. Now, hours later, our second daughter had the same terrible infection. She was the one who would need intravenous penicillin immediately. She was the one who would need to fight for her life.

We pulled up to the doors of the emergency department at Galmi Hospital and the staff sprang into action. They rushed Emily to the operating room for resuscitation, but the truth was obvious. Pep and I admitted to one another what we had known for the last half of the trip. I threw myself across Emily's motionless body on the hospital stretcher, giving her one last hug, wailing in tears, in complete anguish. Our beautiful child had died.

Our friends and colleagues stepped in to help and comfort. The focus quickly moved to Bethany. Doctors were assessing her, getting an intravenous line inserted, giving orders for the antibiotic treatment to begin.

Bethany was very sick and became worse each hour. Normally, there was not a pediatrician at Galmi Hospital, but here's where the miracles became tangible. I'm convinced it was by divine intervention that a pediatrician from Boston, Dr. Pete Johnsen, had just arrived in Galmi the evening before. He was perfectly trained to take over Bethany's care.

Bethany's kidneys seemed to have shut down. She stopped urinating and became all puffed up. She probably had something called Waterhouse-Friderichsen syndrome, a condition I recalled from medical school pathology lectures. It occurs in severe meningococcal infections when there is bleeding into the adrenal glands, and it can be deadly.

There was no intensive care unit at Galmi Hospital, but the doctors set up a makeshift ICU in a storage room. It was the size of a walk-in closet, but there was room to deliver high-quality critical care. They inserted a central line in one of Bethany's neck veins. It was an efficient way to deliver intravenous fluids, monitor the right flow, and take blood tests. Dr. Johnsen hooked up a tank of welding oxygen from the maintenance shop along with an improvised bubbler and nasal prongs to increase her oxygen levels.

They set up a cot beside her where Pep and I would take turns through the night. Just before midnight, a couple of the doctors came to see us. They expressed their profound sympathy about Emily's death, and then they told us that we should prepare for the worst. They did not expect Bethany to survive.

What they didn't factor into their thinking is that Bethany is a fighter. From the time she was a tiny infant we knew she had a strong will, and we considered that to be an asset, not a problem. She has a determination to defy expectations, the spunk to do what others believe cannot be done. Pep and I saw that indomitability in Bethany as she fought for her life in that cobbled-together ICU. Her spirit and grit, the medical miracle of penicillin, the meticulous care of doctors and nurses, the prayers of thousands of people around the world, and God's grace were what kept Bethany alive. We experienced an exceptional range of emotions.

We had a funeral for Emily on March 12, 1991, the morning after her death and exactly twenty-five years to the day since my brother Gary had died. We were surrounded by love and compassion, from missionary colleagues, from hospital staff, and from countless people in the village of Galmi. They came in large numbers to greet us and to grieve with us. We sang my favourite hymn, "Be Still My Soul," to the beautiful tune of *Finlandia* by Jean Sibelius. It was on that day, through the harmonies of that musical prayer, that I first truly understood the healing bond of shared grief.

After the funeral service, we took Emily's body to be buried on a hillside west of Galmi village. The hospital carpenter had made a wooden box in her size, and her body was lowered in that box into the rocky ground. A small group of friends stood in a circle. We wept. We prayed. I wept for the terrible, shocking reality that our innocent daughter Emily was no longer with us. She had left us far too soon.

I prayed for Bethany. Throughout the funeral and burial, our second daughter was fighting for her life over at the hospital. She had made it through the night, but it was still uncertain if she would survive. I pleaded with God to heal her. I wondered how I could go on living if I had to return to the graveside to bury our second child the next day.

We were not the only ones praying. By this time, friends and family around the world had heard about Emily's death and Bethany's illness. For months and even years later, we would meet people who told us that they had prayed for us and for Bethany at that time.

You may not believe in God, and perhaps you think praying is nothing more than a psychological balm. I believe in the power of prayer with my whole heart and mind. I know Bethany survived because of modern medical treatment, including antibiotics. I am both a medical doctor and a person of faith, and it is not incompatible to believe her survival was a miracle, linked to the prayers of thousands of people who joined us in pleading to God on our behalf.

The morning after the funeral, outside the small trailer on the hospital compound where Pep and I had taken a few moments to get dressed for another day, we stepped outside and were stunned to see a long line of Nigerien friends, neighbours, and colleagues. They had come with words of comfort. We heard an unusual greeting that day. Each person would look in our eyes and shake our hands, then shake their head as they spoke slowly: Gaisuwa maigida. Gaisuwa uwargida. Yi hankuri. Sai hankuri. The latter part means: Be patient. There is only patience.

Patience. In the face of losing your child. In the face of another child fighting for her life. Be patient. I'm sure I still don't grasp the full significance of that greeting, although it strikes me as being connected at its core to the first stanza of the serenity prayer, which asks God to grant us grace to accept the things we cannot change. You can't deny how awful it is. You can't deny the guilt and regret, or the big wound that is forever open and raw in your heart. But at some point, you have to move on. You have to forgive yourself and try not to dwell on what you might have done differently. You have to stop torturing yourself with imagining what life would be like if she were still alive. You have to be patient and accept reality. It happened. It's the worst loss of my life. I can't bring her back. But I can do things that will honour her life. I can look around and quickly see that I'm not the only person who has had pain and loss. In fact, that's exactly what I saw that day—dozens of other parents who had faced similar grief, and much greater loss and suffering than I would ever know.

At that time in Niger, almost three out of every ten babies born would not live to see their fifth birthday. It seemed almost every Nigerienne woman I knew had experienced the death of at least one of her children. Our loss was profound. But we were not special. We had entered into a new bond with our friends and colleagues. We were newly united in grief.

Since that moment, I have not been able to separate my grief about losing Emily from a sense of heartache about the world, and so many little ones who leave too soon. I cry at almost every funeral I attend—even if I wasn't necessarily that close to the person who died—because it reminds me how fragile life is, and what a gift each person is. The fact that it hurts so much when our loved ones leave us is a testament to the deep joy of loving them so much. To love is to let yourself be susceptible to pain. But I would never forgo the pain if it meant that I had to give back the love. I will keep loving and keep risking. I will keep my heart open, so stretched it could break.

While we were devastated by grief over the death of Emily, we were equally overwhelmed with relief and gratitude for the survival of Bethany. Of those who do survive meningococcemia, a significant number have serious long-term consequences, including hearing loss, amputations, and neurological deficits. The medical team at Galmi stabilized Bethany, but they were worried about how long they could safely provide ongoing intensive care. They arranged a medical evacuation, and so, three days after Emily's death, we flew back to Toronto. Bethany was accompanied by a doctor who managed her care and delivered medications through an intravenous line that had been surgically inserted in her lower leg. After several days in a Toronto hospital, she had a full recovery—except for a few scars from that procedure and from the hemorrhages where she had bled under her skin.

When I reflect on the greatest blessings of my life, I count Bethany's survival among them. We found out later that several children from the Soura neighbourhood we'd visited before Emily died had contracted meningococcal illnesses that week. I don't know how many survived. I don't know how many managed to access good medical care. I am quite sure none of them had the advantages we had, including the ability to fly out of the country to take our child to a specialized care hospital.

This reality marked an awakening. I always knew the world was deeply unfair, that humanity has not been established on a level playing field. But now I lived it with raw emotion. I was on the side of the field with a much better deal, but the people who were disadvantaged through no fault of their own were my friends, my colleagues, and my neighbours in Niger. Whether you live or die from meningococcemia is linked to your access to medical care, which in turn is linked to your affluence and your country of birth. Those disparities persist.

Emily's death and Bethany's survival changed me more than any other single experience of my life. To be well in the wake of that pain, I had to make meaning of those mixed emotions of grief and gratitude. I had to confront the distorted balance of justice on the planet. I will forever grieve the loss of our child who took her last breath on a desert highway in southern Niger. But her death showed me how much work there is to do, and that I cannot passively accept such an unjust world. I decided to devote the rest of my life to the pursuit of fairness, to help us move in any small way toward a world where toddlers don't die at such high rates in places like Niger.

In retrospect, I understand that the ability to make meaning of Emily's death was a key to making the grief bearable. I expect that's why the Elders and community members who designed the FNMWC Framework placed the concept of meaning at the core of mental wellness. Obviously, my experience of loss is not comparable to the existential threats and suffering that First Nations have withstood over many generations. The point is that, regardless of the adversity's scale, you have to contemplate its meaning in order to persevere.

I've struggled to define the meaning of the word *meaning*, in the context of being at the centre of mental wellness. The best I can come up with is that, in order to be well, you must make sense of your surroundings and experiences, your joy and your pain, your history and your apparent future.

Meaning is the answer you get when you ask questions about the life you've got. The ability to make meaning of unexpected events is at the core of mental and spiritual wellness. Meaning is how you make sense of your circumstances. It's the explanations you assemble from your perspective on life, both rational and intuitive. When you struggle to make sense of reality, but you know there's an answer somewhere, meaning is what you seek. And meaning is not simply about the material world, or the puzzles of the human condition. When the splendour and power of the natural world overwhelm your senses, you also long to discern the meaning of it all.

In the rush and routines of contemporary Canadian adulthood, there is not much quiet space to contemplate meaning. Perhaps we prefer not to pause and do the hard work of understanding our own condition, for fear of what we might uncover or, worse still, for fear that we would find no meaning. Even so, I've found that life has a way of jolting me out of my routines periodically, of forcing me to figure things out, to restore equilibrium and make meaning of the events around me.

The only way I could make meaning of Emily's death was to put it in the context of a bigger grief—the heartache of millions of children and adults who die each year of preventable and treatable causes. Emily's death hardened my resolve to commit my life's work to health for all. My quest for global justice led me to a series of initiatives that have given meaning to my life. In 2004, I launched Give a Day to World AIDS to raise money for people in sub-Saharan Africa living with HIV. From 2008 to 2014, I helped launch a family medicine training program in Ethiopia. Ultimately, my passion for health equity led me to federal politics. Nothing can change what happened to Emily. But the way I can make sense of the helpless reality of her death is by helping someone else, by doing what I can to nudge us ever closer to a fairer world.

CHAPTER 7

Purpose

I found one of the only open seats at the departure gate in Toronto's Pearson Airport and sat down just as a physical sensation of panic came over me. I had already checked my luggage and passed through security. There was less than an hour to wait before boarding. Underneath that wave of anxiety was the question of whether I was doing something terribly reckless. I was about to fly to Paris, then on to Niamey, the capital city of Niger. From there I would travel by road nine hundred kilometres east to the city of Zinder, where I was going to spend two months working with Médecins Sans Frontières, treating children at risk of dying from severe malnutrition.

It was not the long trip that worried me, or the gruelling work that awaited, or the remote location. Our family had previously lived in Niger for almost a decade, so I was comfortable with the hot, dry climate. I was familiar with the culture, and I still remembered how to speak in Hausa. The reason I felt sick was that I was leaving four children behind. They were aged fifteen, twelve, ten, and four. I was the mother of a four-year-old and I was leaving Canada for two months. What kind of a mother was I?

I knew with certainty that Pep was fully capable of caring for the kids. He cooks and runs a household better than I. He had just started a new job in the national radio newsroom of the Canadian Broadcasting Company (CBC). There was a union lockout that summer of 2005, so he had some flexibility in scheduling his hours. He would figure it all out, and my parents would help. The well-being of the children was not at risk. I was the one with a problem. I was conflicted by the tension between my roles as mother and doctor, and it had escalated to a point of panic.

It was the flash onset of an identity crisis—a predicament about purpose. I had spent fifteen years seeing myself first as a mother (and wife), and second as a doctor. Abruptly, I was going to flip that image, and not even see my children for two months. I would have almost no ability to phone home. Opportunities to send emails would be limited. Who was I? Was I a mother, devoted to our four beautiful children? Or was I chasing a self-centred delusion, fashioning myself as a humanitarian doctor, dropping my other responsibilities to live on the edge of the desert, trying to save lives? Was it possible to be both a good mother and a woman with a career that led her to the other side of the world for two months straight? Why was I even asking myself these questions? Didn't men leave their families for work reasons all the time, being deployed for months on end? Did they experience an identity crisis at a time like this? Maybe they did, but I had never heard any of them say so. The questions swirled in my mind.

Eventually, I boarded the plane. It was an uneasy start to a journey that would be another turning point for me. I was about to discover that my daily purpose could shift, that there are many acceptable ways to be a doctor, a leader, and a mom. I needed to learn I could be both a good mother and also someone who loves her career and finds satisfaction from focusing on that.

The plan to go to Niger had not been in the works for very long. I had been following the news of a terrible wave of drought affecting the country. While on vacation at my parents' cottage, I saw that MSF was urgently seeking doctors to help. I read reports of the situation and had a strong impulse to respond. The time between my call to the MSF Toronto office and that flight to Niamey was only a few weeks. MSF Suisse had set up operations in the city of Zinder. The team estimated that over ten thousand children in the region met the criteria for severe malnutrition. They had set up two large inpatient facilities in the city. The other children were cared for in the surrounding villages. I was assigned to one of the travelling teams, going to a different town or village each day, six days a week, to assess and treat children with severe malnutrition. We brought the sickest ones back to the city to be admitted. The expatriates on my team were a Cameroonian doctor and an American nurse. We also had Nigerien nurses and logisticians who would travel with us each day. Between us, we would assess two hundred to three hundred children each day.

The children most at risk of severe malnutrition were between eighteen months and two years of age. They had been weaned from the breast and were not getting enough calories or protein. Most of them weighed only four or five kilograms.

Recently, I looked back at an early message to my family about a ten-month-old who weighed only 2.5 kilograms. I described others as "literally just skin and bones. When you pick up the little ones, it is like lifting a wee skeleton. Some of the ones we bring in for admission are severely dehydrated (tons of watery diarrhea) so in addition to their skinniness, their skin is all dry and wrinkly. Once they are well enough, they get put on a feeding program—first with F100 milk and then with this amazing supplement called Plumpy'nut which is a high-protein paste that tastes like sweet peanut butter."

In other messages to Pep and the kids, I would copy diary entries, like the one below:

Wednesday, September 21, 2005

Today, there were more who were so critical they needed to be transferred to Zinder. We were 3 hours from Zinder and it's a rough ride back. We had seven babies and moms sent ahead of us in the truck with 2 nurses. We came along a little later and caught up with them as the truck is slow. The sickest one with cerebral malaria had already died on the route. We were more than halfway to Zinder, so we decided to keep that mom and babe with us. I took the other really sick one with its mom, and the dead baby and its mom, into the 4x4 with me. It was kind of a striking moment for me—bringing back memories of Emily. Beside me in the back seat of the 4x4 is the one mom whose baby has severe malnutrition, kwashiorkor, and malaria—doing what we can to keep him alive. His hands and feet are swollen and cracked. The baby is lapsing in and out of consciousness. Beside her is the other mom with the dead baby wrapped in a cloth in her arms. I can't help but wonder why the world doesn't care about these children. For some reason my mind thought back to a news story I heard on the BBC 2 days ago about NASA re-opening the space program with a goal to get back to the moon by 2020. How do we have the brains and resources to reach the moon, but we can't find the brains, resources, and human willpower to ensure that in the year 2005, mothers and babies in Niger should not have to live and die like this? We did make it to Zinder with the kwashiorkor baby who was admitted to intensive care.

It went on like that for two months, working six days a week, travelling to villages in the Zinder area each day to assess hundreds of children, trying to identify the ones most at risk of dying so they could be brought back to the temporary hospital. Those who didn't meet the criteria of extreme malnutrition would be given beans, rice, vegetable oil, and the ubiquitous Plumpy'nut paste. They would be treated for malaria or other conditions.

I was consumed by my work. It was one of the most intensely focused periods of clinical activity in my life, with long, exhausting days, driven by a sense of the urgency to save lives. That pace of work would be unsustainable for most people, and it was for me. But I learned many things through it—about people, about the ways of the world, about the work I wanted to do. I learned that it was okay for my daily purpose, the activities to which I would devote my time, to be related to my career as much as to my family. That did not mean I was a bad mother.

I will never regret having more than a decade of my life where my primary daily focus and purpose was motherhood.

I loved that season, pouring my time and energy into the lives of Bethany, Jacob, David, and Lydia. I worked at my medical practice part-time through all those years, serving my community (whether in Niger or in Stouffville). But it reached the point where our children needed me less—and I wanted to do more. The 2005 MSF mission reminded me of the satisfaction of my work in global health. I also knew it was time to reflect on my clinical career and whether I was fully addressing my purpose in that space.

Purpose is what gets you out of bed each morning. It's what you do every day, how you structure your time, activities, and behaviours. As clinical psychologist Dr. Christopher Mushquash told me, simply getting your day together is an act of wellness. According to the Indigenous Wellness Framework, developed by Elder Jim Dumont and Dr. Carol Hopkins, and a precursor to the FNMWC, the purpose of your daily life might be a job, your education, your caregiving activities, or even your cultural practices of being and doing.[1] Your purpose could include tending a garden or caring for a pet.

I have thought a lot about purpose because I've been lucky enough to have a lot of options when it comes how I spend my days. It is easier said than done, to know your purpose. But the quest is an exercise worth pursuing. If we look beyond daily choices—to consider career choices, for example—I have found the notion of purpose can be helpful when it comes to distinguishing among the conflicting options of how and where to use our time.

There have been a few times when I've had to make hard decisions about my purpose and where my priorities should lie. Over a range of different roles—as a wife, a mother, a family doctor, a former politician, and now a university dean—it has occasionally been hard for me to decide where to devote myself.

Late in 2006, I hit a patch of burnout in my clinical practice. I'll spare you the details, but suffice it to say I was unsettled. I tried to explain this to Pep, who has commendable patience for my recurring restlessness. I announced that I wasn't satisfied with the idea of spending the rest of my life as a suburban family doctor unless something changed. I considered my options and came up with these: (1) I could go back to school to start a master's degree and perhaps later a Ph.D; (2) I could go into politics; or (3) we could go back to Africa, either to Niger or elsewhere.

By serendipity, there was a doctor doing a locum with our group that winter who was working on a master's degree at the University of Toronto. She recommended the program and said I should apply. So, I did. I started taking courses, while working almost full-time in the clinic. Five years later, I graduated as a master of public health. In retrospect, I am shocked at how busy those years were, but they were so satisfying. I was a sponge soaking up the scholarly content, and that re-entry into academic medicine changed my direction in significant ways.

I took several courses about medical education and began to contemplate the intriguing world of teaching and learning in the health professions. Before then I had hosted an occasional student in my work, but I started having more medical students, family medicine residents, and learners in other programs, such as nurse practitioners and physician assistants. I made the helpful discovery that I felt much more fulfilled in my work when it had an impact beyond the clinical service.

Teaching the next generation of health professionals restored for me the joy of medicine.

A snowball of opportunities in the hospital and the university came my way, and I piled them all on, each one making me happier in spite of working more than ever. It wasn't the hard work or the long hours that had made me burn out. It was a lack of work satisfaction and a sense of not being able to improve the systems around me. The more responsibility I took on, the more tools in my hand so I could fix things, the more I enjoyed my work.

That theme of improving systems—whether clinical, educational, or political—to improve people's health has essentially been my purpose ever since. I learned that we don't have to accept the status quo—for ourselves or for others—especially if the structures around us have an adverse impact on wellness or quality of life.

What that looks like in terms of daily purpose—time, activities, behaviours, or what gets me out of bed in the morning—has varied over the past couple of decades, but having a predominant theme has been really helpful for decision-making and for capturing new opportunities. To accomplish my overarching purpose, I've had to think about who holds the levers of power to change the systems around me, and whether I could get my hands on some of those levers.

Your purpose is not the same as your job or even your role. Jobs change, sometimes abruptly. When I went into politics, it was not for the job or the title; it was for the purpose of improving health and social systems. I was extremely sad when my political career ended in 2019, but the circumstances surrounding that transition did not sway me from my purpose.

I was soon blessed with a new opportunity to improve people's health, this time through the academic sector, where there are also many levers to make system-wide changes.

I don't want to leave the impression that you need access to powerful societal structures to have purpose, and therefore wellness. Having a purpose for life or a purpose for each day contributes to well-being no matter what that purpose is—from political change to planetary health, from raising children to writing music. When I asked Dr. Carol Hopkins how purpose contributes to mental wellness, she said that having purpose means you understand you are not in this world by mistake. You have deliberate choices to make every day. Those decisions have an impact, for good or ill, on people around you— and, she noted, they also have an impact on the land.

I'll end this part with something Martin Luther King Jr. said to a group of students back in 1967: "If it falls to your lot to be a street sweeper, sweep streets like Michelangelo painted pictures. Sweep streets like Beethoven composed music. Sweep streets like Leontyne Price sings before the Metropolitan Opera. And sweep streets like Shakespeare wrote poetry. Sweep streets so well that all the host of Heaven and Earth will have to pause and say, 'Here lived a great street sweeper, who swept his job well.'"[2]

PART THREE

Social

CHAPTER 8

Health beyond Medicine

Among the people who choose to call Canada home, who contribute to our economy and our rich tapestry of multiple cultures, is a tall, quiet man I'll call Tobe. A few years ago, Tobe and his family fled their homeland on the African continent because they feared for their lives.

Tobe grew up on that vast continent in the context of a brutal civil war that led to food shortages. He remembers the swollen belly of his childhood, caused by protein deficiency. The condition is called kwashiorkor. To treat the malnutrition, the old women in his village taught the children to eat lizards and crickets, which offered some protein. To earn support for his family, Tobe had started to work in the local market by age thirteen. His father wasn't home much, because his job was "on the high seas," but he told Tobe that he must learn to read. So, the boy managed to study at home and eventually obtained the equivalent of a high school diploma.

Tobe grew up with almost nothing in the way of financial resources, and no social capital—that is, no favours he could count on from his personal connections. But his parents taught

him that capital comes from diligence and integrity. They clev-
erly pointed out that these resources have extra value because
of their scarcity. Tobe packed that capital with him on the day
he hid in a truck and made his way to the city as a young man
seeking work. Diligence and integrity came in handy when he
landed a clerical job in a private consulting practice.

From there, his story unfolded like a Hollywood movie. The
self-taught young man with a mind for numeracy was discovered by a major international accounting firm, which recruited
him into an apprenticeship, in spite of him having no college
degree. They later sent him abroad to get his qualifications
as a chartered professional accountant. He became an expert
in computer auditing and took these skills back to his home
country. Unfortunately, his expertise in system security, computer auditing, and financial controls were not always appreciated there. When he unearthed financial fraud and refused to
cover it up, he made himself a target. After receiving more than
one death threat, Tobe realized that neither he nor his family
was safe.

Tobe knew he had to seek asylum outside his homeland,
and Canada was his first choice. He escaped with his family,
first to the United States. For the next portion of the journey,
the family split up. He fled with one of his sons to Roxham
Road in upstate New York where he had heard he could cross
on foot into Canada. The father and son became two statistics added to the thousands of asylum seekers who crossed the
border that year, looking for refuge in a country with a reputation for taking its international humanitarian obligations seriously. From the Quebec side of Roxham Road, Tobe and his
son were loaded onto a bus and taken to a shelter in Montreal.

They stayed in that shelter for six weeks and spoke to almost no one. There was food, but little guidance about navigating the next steps. Tobe tried to begin the process of filing a refugee claim but was making little progress. It was on a phone call to the Canadian Red Cross that someone told him about Matthew House Ottawa (MHO), a charitable organization dedicated to working with homeless refugee claimants, giving them support to find jobs and homes of their own. Tobe and his son made their way to Ottawa and sought shelter at MHO. Within a week, their refugee process had traction as the program managers reviewed their papers and helped them file the proper documents.

MHO has an impressive story itself. It has grown rapidly—from operating two houses in Ottawa in 2021 to having thirteen houses and ninety beds by 2023. They offer personalized, wrap-around attention. This includes connecting residents with legal aid and a lawyer for filing a refugee claim; assisting with applications for welfare support until clients find work; arranging volunteer opportunities to assist with resumé-building; and providing food, shelter, safety, relationships, and community.

Tobe arrived just as MHO was starting a newcomer training and employment program. Through the program, he secured a part-time job for thirteen weeks at the MHO Furniture Bank (a remarkable place that recycles used furniture so that when people find housing, they will also have some basics like a bed and a place to sit). The work gave Tobe some Canadian experience to put on his resumé as he looked for work using the accounting skills he'd brought to Canada. Currently, he's doing seasonal tax work—and paying taxes himself. Meanwhile, he's launching a start-up to train people in his home country with skills for computer auditing. Tobe is now renting a home with his son and hoping they can soon be reunited with his wife and other sons.

All of that took about five months—from arriving at a homeless shelter in downtown Montreal, to being employed, housed, and on a waiting list for his refugee claim to be examined.

I've been impressed with the work of MHO, which is led by Allan Reesor-McDowell. The cost to run the program is about $800 per person per month. The average length of stay is less than six months. Nearly every resident finishes their time at MHO with a home and a job. In 2022, they moved seventy-nine people from a state of homelessness to a path of integration, productivity, and health. With the rapid growth of the program, they expect higher numbers each year. While only 30 percent of the program is government-funded, this is the kind of investment we should be happy to support. It has a good return.

The impact of MHO is small in the big picture of a very serious problem related to the housing of refugees who are seeking asylum in Canada. The whole issue reached a crisis point in the summer of 2023 when more than a hundred people were sleeping on the streets of Toronto outside an overburdened shelter intake centre, as orders of governments argued about which of them was responsible for helping. In the meantime— thank goodness—business owners, community agencies, and faith-based groups stepped in to assist. Leaving people to sleep on the streets is obviously not good for their health, not appreciated by neighbours, and not necessary if there were a more organized, proactive approach to the treatment of asylum seekers. That is not to mention the international commitments to which Canada is obliged under the United Nations Convention (1951) and Protocol (1967) relating to the status of refugees.

Canada leads the world in the resettlement of refugees. More than half of them come to Canada through private sponsorship. Others are offered safe haven through a government-organized program such as the one developed for Syrian refugees starting in 2015.

A third category, and arguably the refugees who face the greatest health risks, are those who arrive uninvited. This includes tens of thousands of people who find their way to Canada via precarious channels, such as irregular border crossings—which is how Tobe and his son arrived. It is refugees in this third category who have found themselves living on the streets of Canadian cities because there is little in the way of a system to manage their existence. Do policy-makers believe that the flow of unsolicited people seeking safe haven in Canada will eventually stop? Or do governments fear that establishing a better structure of housing and services for asylum seekers will send the message that we've put out a welcome mat? The rationale for the current lack of coordination is not clear, and it is not in keeping with our obligations. Canada's international commitments require us to adhere to minimum standards in the treatment of refugees. This includes the right to housing, work, and education.

Our rationale for the fair treatment of refugees should go beyond our humanitarian obligations. As a country, we have benefited greatly from the integration of people who were forced to leave their homelands. Most of us can only imagine arriving, uninvited, on the figurative doorstep of another country with a plea to be let in, to be given a fair hearing. People like Tobe arrive in Canada by the most fascinating pathways. Our country becomes richer for their contributions. We can surely be more organized about the process for their integration into society.

What would have happened to Tobe and his son if they had not been referred to MHO? What was their alternative path? Without the right support, we know the health status of refugees often deteriorates after arriving in Canada. This is attributed to the stress of adapting to a new country and culture.[1] "The mother of all diseases is stress," said Tobe, explaining how finding shelter and assistance at MHO "helped me become calm." His blood pressure returned to normal. MHO helped him find work. He found a home. He found community. With a job and an income, he had better options for nutritious food and even recreation. With his basic needs met, he was more likely to be healthy, and the community would benefit from his contributions to society.

Tobe's story is a simple example of how our pursuit of wellness requires much more than investments in medical care. Policy-makers who oversee the well-being of a province or a country need to focus enormous resources and attention on better health care systems. But those services can't make up for all the gaps that exist in our social systems. We need laws, policies, and practices designed with the well-being of the whole population in mind. Public policies that affect the health of one person or group directly have an impact on the wellness of others indirectly. In theory, democratic leaders consider the best interests of everyone as they write and rewrite the rules that govern us. In practice, the rules don't work for everyone.

Canada has a strong history of beneficial social structures. But it's hard to design and uphold structures that ensure the wellness of all people so that no one is left behind. In this part,

I'm going to explore some of these social constructs, but with a focus on those people still at risk of being sidelined by our systems. Attention to the health of people who might otherwise be marginalized will simultaneously make the country better for all.

I learned these lessons from experience, not from a classroom. As a medical student, I had soaked up volumes of scientific knowledge. Sitting near the front in the old lecture hall of the Medical Sciences Building at Western, I would focus my full attention and take notes. We learned fascinating facts. For example, I recall trying to comprehend the astonishing loop of Henle, which functions inside our kidneys every day, faithfully cleaning out waste to be sent out of the body in the form of urine, and keeping our bodily fluids balanced to the right pH setting. That was one of countless remarkable features of the human body that were planted into our brains.

Medical school in the 1980s was a whirlwind journey through the biomedical sciences: anatomy, biochemistry, microbiology, pharmacology, physiology, and more. But I don't recall a single lecture that would fall into the category of what we would now call the social determinants of health. If we talked about the impact of housing, income, jobs, or education on health, I sure don't remember it. That was deemed outside the scope of what a doctor needed to learn.

It wasn't until we spent nine years in Niger in the 1990s that I put things into perspective. Despite everything I knew as a medical doctor, I quickly came to see that there were much more powerful forces at work, determining who would be sick and who would be well. Even if we could have flown in a multitude of health workers and offered the best diagnostic and treatment services in the world, the people of Niger would still have had poor health outcomes, and they would expect to live shorter lives than Canadians would. During the decade we lived there, life expectancy at birth rose from forty-one to forty-eight years of age. It's now sixty-two years.[2] Meanwhile, during the years that we were in Niger, life expectancy in Canada rose from seventy-seven to seventy-nine years, and it's now eighty-three.

Possible explanations for the shorter life expectancy in Niger were obvious from even a cursory observation. In the 1990s, more than 80 percent of its people were living in extreme poverty, defined as living below the international poverty line of $2.15 per day.[3] Even in the late 1990s, many of us spent more than that for a cup of coffee. I saw the impact of that poverty in the form of malnourished children and adults, or in the mud-brick houses that would collapse under the pressure of heavy rains. This was compounded by so many other social, political, and geographic factors: extremely low rates of literacy, marked gender-based discrimination, a weak democracy, a climate unfit for agricultural productivity, and more.

Just as I was making sense of this, wondering why no one ever taught me this perspective in medical school, a book was published in 1999 in the United Kingdom by Michael Marmot and Richard Wilkinson called *Social Determinants of Health*. In their text, the authors articulated the phenomena I had observed in real life. Health is the result of so much more than health care.

So, twenty-five years ago, the evidence was all there on paper, in an authoritative textbook, to show that if we want a healthy population, we need to invest in the upstream factors that determine wellness. The Canadian government has not hesitated to affirm the importance of the social determinants of health and has listed the key ones on its public health website.[4] They are:

- income and social status
- employment and working conditions
- education and literacy
- childhood experiences
- physical environments
- social supports and coping skills
- healthy behaviours
- access to health services
- biology and genetic endowment
- gender
- culture
- race/racism

The reality is that almost every law or policy in the hands of government decision-makers could be evaluated for its impact on the health of the population. In fact, there is a global movement drawing attention to this. It's called Health in All Policies (HIAP). One objective of the HIAP perspective is to remind policymakers that investments in housing or education, for example, yield not only their direct benefits but also their downstream benefits of improved health outcomes.

Attention to the social determinants of health matters because these issues are the building blocks of a peaceful and productive society. We won't be healthy without them. And for those who view economic considerations as the primary metrics to evaluate public policy, the HIAP lens is worth considering because of the opportunity to reduce health spending in Canada.

To grasp why this matters to our economic outlook, consider that, if we measure spending on health services alone, Canada's total spending has ballooned over the quarter-century since Marmot and Wilkinson's textbook was published. We spent $90 billion in current Canadian dollars in 1999. It's up to $330 billion per year according to the current forecast.[5] That works out to $8,563 per Canadian, placing us among the highest-spending countries in the Organisation for Economic Co-operation and Development.[6,7]

How can we decrease that per capita cost for health? In part one, I argued that we could save money and achieve better health outcomes if we oriented our health care systems in the direction of primary care. And we can be even more efficient in our public spending if we focus further upstream, on the socio-economic drivers of health, or the lack thereof.

A recent report by the Commonwealth Fund reviewed the evidence around the idea that investing in housing would yield good returns for health.[8] They found strong evidence that providing people who are homeless, or at risk of becoming homeless, with housing will reduce hospital admissions and visits to the emergency department. One study estimated for every dollar spent on supportive housing there was a health system savings of $1.57.

Michael Marmot—now a "Sir" in the United Kingdom—and many others, including Canada's former minister of health and welfare Monique Bégin, have already made that case, and it should be heeded. They were part of the Commission on Social Determinants of Health established by the World

Health Organization in 2005. With a brevity that is atypical of such international statements, the Commission delivered its final report[9] in 2008 with just three recommendations for policy-makers:

1. Improve daily living conditions;
2. Tackle the inequitable distribution of power, money, and resources; and
3. Measure and understand the problem and assess the impact of action.

Canada needs that kind of clarity to be front of mind for the people who decide our public priorities. Perhaps we should create a poster with those directives and have it plastered to the walls of the cabinet rooms of governments across the country, to be read aloud before every meeting begins. Then again, why stop with cabinet rooms? Maybe the same recommendations should be considered in all our public institutions, and, beyond that, in the boardrooms of corporations or civil society organizations that commit themselves to the public good.

CHAPTER 9

The Sound of Silence

Easter Sunday of 2020 started much like it did every year, with me hiding store-bought chocolate eggs in fairly obvious places around our living room, kitchen, and dining room, this time at our townhouse in Stouffville. Lydia was the only child at home, and she was sleeping in. Pep was at work in the newsroom at CBC's Toronto headquarters. Once I finished my job as Easter Bunny, I settled in to enjoy a cup of coffee in peace and quiet.

At 7:42 a.m., I received this text from my friend Leea Nutson:

> Hi there. Sorry to be texting you so early, but the director of Participation House has asked me to contact you to see if you can help. They are desperate for staff, and she is getting frantic.

We were one month into the realization that the COVID-19 pandemic was going to be no ordinary outbreak of an infectious disease. Those were the days with horrific numbers of cases and deaths in the institutions that are home to the most marginalized citizens, long before vaccines were available. Leea's adult daughter Bergen Nutson lived at Participation House, Markham (PHM), a group home for adults with complex intellectual and developmental disabilities. Bergen and the other residents of PHM were at very high risk of contracting COVID-19, and in fact dozens of them did. At the main campus, forty out of forty-two residents acquired COVID-19 in April of that year. By the end of May, six had died.

Leea's text was a cry for help. With the news of this huge outbreak, 90 percent of the facility's staff had to abandon their work, either because they were symptomatic or infected themselves, or because it suddenly became clear that it was not wise for personal support workers (PSWs) to be on staff at more than one place, so they decided to continue at another facility. Ten people from management were available to assist with care roles, and they were stretched beyond their limits.

I know Leea did not expect me to show up personally in response to her text. She was hoping I could help find nurses or PSWs or bring the need to the attention of the media or government.

But the situation was grave, and my basic instincts as a health care professional told me I had to show up in person. My political career had recently ended and I had not yet started my job at Queen's University, so I had flexible time. After a phone conversation with the executive director, Shelley Brillinger, I got myself dressed and headed to the site to see what I could do. That was the beginning of a six-week experience on the front lines of one of the worst pandemic outbreaks in the Greater Toronto Area.

I walked into a facility where 95 percent of the residents had become positive for COVID-19 in a matter of weeks. At that stage of the pandemic, it seemed no one could get enough personal protective equipment (PPE). No vaccines had been developed. There were no treatments. The residents of this home required help with virtually every activity of daily living: eating, drinking, washing, or moving. Every person who sat at the side of the residents to feed and care for them knew that they were at high risk of acquiring the infection themselves. But most of all, we knew that these residents were at high risk of dying. All of them had other serious medical conditions in addition to their COVID-19 infection.

My notes from the first meeting that day demonstrate the level of anxiety we felt.

> *42 residents, only 4 can walk*
> *Only 2 nurses left (Glenda on days, Cindy on evenings)—*
> *need at least 7*
> *PSWs—need 8–12 per shift—could do 3–6 overnight*
> *Supplies—Cavi wipes, scrubs, ppe, O_2 sats, concentrated O_2*
> *Testing—who needs to be swabbed?*
> *Goals of care—who can call families?*
> *Need to lock it down*

After the briefing, I went to the resident rooms to assess those with signs of fever, fatigue, and coughing.[1] There were so few workers to provide care. PHM was not designed or intended to be a medical facility. It is home for forty-two people. The only way we could support the residents was to rapidly acquire new caregivers to provide high-quality, home-based care.

We contacted every possible organization or agency in a hunt for health professionals. We put out an SOS for more PPE. We ordered oxygen tanks and Symptom Relief Kits.

Tuesday night, I returned after dinner to check the sickest residents. I felt despair at the sight of unfinished meals and beverage trays outside the residents' rooms. Night had fallen and many were asleep, but they had not been fed. I was unsure if this was because people had lost their appetite and thirst or because there simply weren't enough PSWs to feed the residents. From the agitated behaviours and comments of those who could talk, we knew the residents were upset about how the place had been turned upside down. Familiar faces were gone. Strangers were providing care. Someone new every day, every shift. Caregivers wore masks, gloves, and plastic face shields. It's hard to see a smile behind a mask. It's hard to hear words of kindness spoken through a plastic shield. The glasses of unfinished drinks were a symbol of anguish. How would people survive if we couldn't keep them hydrated and fed?

Wednesday evening, I had four phone calls with the nurse on duty. He was worried about a resident named Helen. She was short of breath and couldn't stop coughing. They struggled to keep her oxygen saturation near 90 percent. On top of COVID-19, Helen had heart failure. She was on a high dose of diuretics, and neither she nor her family wanted her to go to the hospital. She hated hospitals. The family wanted her kept comfortable. I reviewed what I would need to do if Helen died in the home. I slept lightly, expecting to be called back to PHM sometime in the night to pronounce a death. To my relief that call never came. Helen made it through the night.

Thursday was the worst day of the first week. I was pulling into the parking lot when I received a couple of texts from Jen Goodwin, who was the charge nurse that day: "Helen is on 6L and sats are 84–88%. We don't have a plan for air hunger. I don't know that we have meds for it either." Then a minute later: "Can you come see Stuart right away?"

Both Helen and Stuart had severe shortness of breath, requiring six litres per minute of oxygen. We hadn't yet acquired oxygen concentrators, so we were using small mobile tanks. At that rate, each of them would use a full tank every hour. I walked into the building, directly to the purple pod where Jen was watching over Stuart, who sat in his wheelchair, coughing frequently. His condition was declining. He looked exhausted and uncomfortable. Stuart had big brown eyes. That morning there was fear in them.

I saw how unstable things were. Jen was running back and forth between these two, changing PPE each time because they were in different pods. In those early days, we barely had assurance from one shift to the next that there would be a nurse on site. PSWs were coming mostly from agencies. So, there were new people every shift who needed to be oriented in their role and instructed in proper PPE use. The small core team of regular PHM staff was getting smaller by the day, as more workers became sick and had to stay home.

When the crisis started, PHM made the bold decision to offer doubled wages for the duration of the outbreak to PSWs who would stay and new ones who would come on board. That was one key to stabilization. Two weeks after the PHM outbreak was declared, the Ontario government announced a policy to increase pay for many front-line health workers during this period.

Still, it was distressingly difficult to meet the staffing needs. Shelley and her team used multiple job portals, agencies, and regional health resources. The Ministry of Children, Community, and Social Services tried to help, and Markham Stouffville Hospital made their human resources team available to assist. I made calls and sent emails to professional nursing organizations. In the context of a pandemic, particularly in the setting of an outbreak, it's a massive undertaking to hire and train a brand-new team of nurses and PSWs in a matter of days.

By that Thursday morning, a week after the outbreak came to light, almost everyone was sick. At least two residents were struggling for their lives. Two had already died after being transferred to hospital. Four others had been admitted. I had no idea when one of the other thirty-four residents might take a turn for the worse. We had more COVID-19-positive cases in our building than most Ontario hospitals were caring for at that time—and we had two nurses on duty.

From the start, we had daily calls with Markham Stouffville Hospital. They were tremendously helpful in sharing supplies of PPE. They made hospital food services available to deliver purées and other meals for residents because PHM had lost their kitchen staff. On Thursday, the daily call with the hospital was a cry for help. I described our situation as a war zone. Perhaps that was a bit dramatic. But we felt fragile.

We decided to transfer both Helen and Stuart to the hospital. I watched one long-time staff member as the paramedics rolled each gurney out the doors. She couldn't say a proper goodbye. She had cared for one of those two residents for over thirty years. They were her family. Would she see them again? Would the hospital staff know the best way to feed and comfort them?

The heartache in her eyes is etched in my mind, along with the faces of all six residents of PHM who died. It's a special person who works for decades in a place like PHM. The nurses and PSWs who make this care possible don't do it because it pays well. It doesn't. They do it because they are people of compassion. They immerse themselves in the vulnerabilities of humanity.

The weeks spent at PHM were a sharp reminder of how inequitable Canadian health care can be in terms of who is prioritized for care. That imbalance existed prior to COVID-19, but it was exacerbated by the pandemic. As an outsider, welcomed into the PHM world in an acute crisis, my comprehension of their long-standing reality was limited, but I saw enough to make me want to speak up, to draw attention to the injustices I observed. I wanted to do something in response to what I witnessed.

In addition to helping with the medical care and logistics, one of the ways I offered to help at PHM was to make myself available to media outlets, in the hope that it would help us resolve the staffing shortage. This was during the first deadly wave of the pandemic. Canadians were justifiably frightened and staying at home if they could, as they had been instructed. News networks were eager for stories from the front lines to feed the public appetite for information about what was going on. Should people panic? How was this going to end?

Shelley and I discussed the pros and cons of going public. What we were going through involved real people, with families who were worried and, in some cases, grieving. We had to ensure their privacy. But we also knew that media attention could help circumstances on the inside. When the outbreak started, Shelley had tried for days to get the full attention of public health authorities and government officials. PSWs and nursing staff were leaving. There was not enough PPE. She feared there would be preventable deaths. No one was returning her calls. When I posted a tweet to say I was going to help, the story finally broke. Media outlets were drawn to the scenario by a former Member of Parliament (MP)—not to mention a former federal minister of health—who chose to provide care in one of the worst-affected congregate-care settings in the country. They sent camera crews. Reporters reached out to me and to PHM, looking for a new angle. Most major networks covered the story at some point.

We agreed to a few TV interviews. The clips ran on a loop with the all-news channels. Suddenly we had attention. Celebrities showed up to deliver PPE. Other volunteers arrived. We had daily calls with ministry officials and public health agents. The situation became hopeful. It's fair to say that our public cry for help may have saved lives. Still, I wondered whether we had used the attention of the media in an ethical manner.

For years, when it comes to the ethics of public advocacy, I've had the words of Nigerian author Chinua Achebe ringing in my ears. In a collection of essays published in 2009, Achebe writes about the role of the media in the telling of tragic stories: "The foreign correspondent is frequently the only means of getting an important story told, or of drawing the world's attention to disasters in the making or being covered up. Such an important role is risky in more ways than one. It can expose the correspondent to actual physical danger; but there is also the moral danger of indulging in sensationalism and dehumanizing the sufferer."[2]

Later, he goes on to say: "[W]hen we are comfortable and inattentive, we run the risk of committing grave injustices absent-mindedly."[3]

When we spoke up about the needs at PHM, we did not want to be inattentive to the risk of dehumanizing those who were suffering. At the same time, we wanted to be helpful. Did I have the right to be a voice on behalf of people whose lives I barely understood?

That question and others rattled around in my brain.

- For whom do I have the right to speak,
  and how do I ensure informed consent?
- What is the link between noisemaking
  and power?
- In the pursuit of health for all, are decision-
  makers hearing the voices of all?
- How can the quiet voices be better heard?

I had learned some things about people living with disabilities before my time at PHM, especially from my niece, Abby Congram who, like Leea's daughter Bergen, lives with Rett syndrome, a neurodevelopmental disorder linked to a genetic mutation that causes severe disability from infancy onward. Like others with Rett syndrome, Abby cannot control her hand movements. She can walk short distances with help but needs to be pushed in a wheelchair otherwise. She needs help with eating, dressing, and bathing.

Another challenging feature of Rett syndrome is the absence of audible speech. Abby cannot speak with her voice. Everyone who knows her will tell you she does speak—her sentiments are clear from the expressions in her bright blue eyes. In recent years, she has learned to communicate with eye-gaze technology, using a speech-generating device. By tracking where her eyes look at the digital screen, the apparatus makes Abby's messages audible. My sister Karen Congram (Abby's mother) and the rest of the family have invested an incalculable number of hours improving the use of the tool. They know Abby has things to say, so she uses the device to make her voice audible. Now she can communicate what she wants to eat, what music she prefers, what style she would like to wear, and what is on her mind.

The fact that Abby and others with Rett syndrome cannot express themselves directly with audible words could be a metaphor for their reality writ large. It is hard for them to be heard. Without someone proactively trying to understand their needs, they might be ignored altogether. Depending on the nature of the disability, some people can and do advocate for themselves. Others are sidelined by society, waiting for someone to notice that they cannot access services to meet their needs. In the case of the residents of PHM in April 2020, they were left waiting to be fed, waiting to be washed, waiting to be prioritized for care.

What is the role of society in response to this reality? What is the role of policy-makers? What is the role of health care professionals? In the case of physicians, they are intentionally trained to be advocates. At Schools of Medicine, we test our learners to ensure they have acquired the skill of advocacy. The Royal College of Physicians and Surgeons defines that competency as follows: "As Health Advocates, physicians contribute their expertise and influence as they work with communities or patient populations to improve health. They work with those they serve to determine and understand needs, *speak on behalf of others* when required, and support the mobilization of resources to effect change [italics added]."[4]

For many years now, I have tried to be an advocate for those whose voices seemed hard to hear—sometime because they literally cannot speak (like Abby), or because they don't have a position or platform from which to be heard. When I was raising money for people living with HIV, I would give speeches and often quote from a book by Laurel Thatcher Ulrich with the charming title *Well-Behaved Women Seldom Make History*. One of my favourite quotations from that book is: "History is a conversation and sometimes a shouting match between present and past, though the voices we most want to hear are barely audible."[5] I would read that and talk about the voices we most needed to hear. The implication was that we should raise our voices (and in some cases raise awareness or raise money) on behalf of those who were not heard.

It was tempting to take pride in considering myself a voice for the voiceless. It's only recently that I was startled by the reflection of Indian author Arundhati Roy, who said, in a speech given upon her acceptance of the Sydney Peace Prize in 2004, "We know of course there's really no such thing as the 'voiceless.' There are only the deliberately silenced, or the preferably unheard."[6] She said that two decades ago, and I wish I'd heard about it much earlier. It forced me to reorient my thoughts.

If we cannot hear the voices of people living with disabilities, is it because they are literally or figuratively voiceless? Or have we deliberately silenced them? Do we go out of our way not to hear them? In the case of the pandemic, did we purposely choose not to listen for the voices of those whose lives were most at risk? If power is activated by noise, what responsibility do policy-makers have to listen for the barely audible? In the context of COVID-19, Canadians have some hard questions to address about the culpability of society and its leaders related to which voices were heard loudest when it seemed everyone's life was at stake.

That first pandemic spring, I learned from the people I met at PHM about the deep systemic disparities that affect their lives. I had often used the term *vulnerable* to describe people living with disabilities, recognizing their increased susceptibility to infection, or their dependence on the assistance of other people. But vulnerability can be misinterpreted as weakness, and it sounds pejorative. The effort it takes to persevere, given those preconditions, shows more strength of character than you'd find inside many of us with the full ability of our bodily functions. I cannot fathom the patience to be mustered, time after time, as you wait for help to get food put in your mouth, to be repositioned in your bed or chair, or to get your soiled clothing refreshed.

More recently, I have come to think the word *vulnerable* does not reflect the people to whom it is attached but rather the category where we, as a society, have placed them. We use the term *vulnerable* as a euphemism for people whose voices we've not made the effort to hear.

I try to avoid the word now. Perhaps, in the spirit of Arundhati Roy, who says that inaudible voices are more likely to have been deliberately silenced, we should only use the word *vulnerable* as an objective modifier, as in *made vulnerable*. To have made some groups vulnerable during the height of the pandemic would be a shameful reflection on our societal biases, so the onus should be on those of us who might have let it be so—and could have stopped it—to examine ourselves.

In the early days of the pandemic, biases such as these were evident, and people died unnecessarily. Many sectors of society were at heightened risk of infection and death (people living in poverty, people without shelter, racialized people, etc.). The categories of those who were particularly susceptible to premature death from COVID-19 include older people, and people living with complex disabilities. Their risks were heightened even more because they were not prioritized. While the focus of attention was on preparing hospitals, their ICUs, and emergency departments for the onslaught of people with COVID-19, hundreds of its victims suffered in group homes and long-term care facilities that did not have adequate staffing, or enough PPE, or sufficient public health supports.

In the first wave of the pandemic, well before vaccines were available, about 80 percent of all Canadian deaths attributed to COVID-19 took place in long-term care and retirement homes.[7] While that was happening, those facilities actually had less access to medical care than usual. There were fewer physician visits at those LTC homes, and patients were transferred to hospital less often than before the pandemic. I hate to hypothesize this, but it's as if we collectively decided that we didn't want older people putting the rest of us at risk, so their care was optional. Or worse still, they were viewed as a burden.

In Canada, the proportion of COVID-19 deaths linked to LTC homes is among the highest rates in the world.[8] It didn't have to be that way, and the lessons learned have yet to be documented by way of an independent review of Canada's pandemic response.[9] Many structural changes need to be made. Some already have been. That includes improving and implementing regulations about the standards of care in LTC facilities and group homes. It includes better policies related to the training, working conditions, and wages of PSWs and other parts of the health workforce.

More fundamental, what's required is an adjustment in societal values. Overall, our country perpetuates an ageist and ableist culture, as confirmed by the ravages of the pandemic. Yet there are some subcultures where older people are cherished, and revered; where people living with disabilities are not only not set aside but rather prioritized for attention and care. There are also families, like that of my niece Abby, whose parents refuse to act as if their daughter can't speak.

What will it take for the values of the broader Canadian society to change? I asked my sister Karen, who is an accessible education specialist, about this. She pointed me to some of the arguments she has studied that suggest that the shift needs to occur in the moral fabric of society.[10] Karen explained to me, by email, that "Empirical evidence isn't going to change the culture. Essentially, people's stories will. It's about literacy, but that's the case for everything about health for all. From my work in inclusive education, teachers and students are changed through empathy. We need to hear each other's stories."

CHAPTER 10

Land, Language, Lineage, Loved Ones

"One newborn every day."

Cora Morgan spoke those words calmly, with no hint of drama. I focused closely to catch every word of her solemn, disturbing message. Cora was dressed all in black and seated at a wooden table that had been covered with a red cloth. To her right was the Grand Chief of the Assembly of Manitoba Chiefs (AMC). To her left was the woman Elder who presided over our meeting. Cora worked for and spoke on behalf of the First Nations Family Advocate Office (FNFAO) in Winnipeg. She continued with her prepared remarks, informing me about the work the organization had done to build the case for urgent changes to child welfare laws, policies, and practices.

One newborn every day. In Manitoba, on average, every single day, at least one First Nations child was being taken from its mother and family, most often at birth. She stated that shocking data point without significant emotion. I had the impression she had already told countless officials about this, and almost nothing had changed. It was painful but old news to Cora and to the assembled Chiefs and others. To me, it was mind-blowing. I could hardly believe it was true. I would later confirm that the exact figure was even a little higher than one per day. Maybe I had even heard that fact before, but it had never sunk in. I had never stopped to picture that each day, every day, a child was being taken away from his or her family.

It was time for me to pay attention. Just two months earlier, in late August 2017, I became Canada's first minister of Indigenous services in an unexpected cabinet shuffle. The rationale for creating this position was provided by the prime minister when he asked me to take on the role. He was acting on a recommendation from the 1996 Royal Commission on Aboriginal Peoples. It was all about restructuring the relationship between the Canadian government and the First Peoples of the land. Here's what those commissioners wrote:

> The federal government will need to undergo some reorganization of its own:
> - The Department of Indian Affairs and Northern Development and the ministerial position that goes with it should be eliminated.
> - A new senior cabinet position, the Minister for Aboriginal **Relations**, and a new Department of Aboriginal Relations should be assigned to negotiate and manage new agreements and arrangements from the federal government's side.

- Another minister, the Minister of Indian and Inuit **Services**, and a new Indian and Inuit Services department should be assigned to deliver the gradually diminishing services coming from the federal level [emphasis added].[1]

Put simply, one cabinet position was eliminated and two new ones were created. The new cabinet minister described in bullet two has the task of better *relationships*. The minister described in bullet three has the task of better *services*.

The specific titles for these new roles when they were introduced in 2017 were slightly different from what had been recommended by the Royal Commission. I was given the job described in the third bullet. Upon careful reading, you'll notice that if the federal government follows the recommendations, the portfolio given to me, the minister of Indigenous services, is to be gradually diminished, and eventually eliminated. It's designed to be short-term.

Getting the federal government out of the business of delivering services for Indigenous Peoples depends on the work of the minister described in the second bullet. This person, the minister of Crown-Indigenous relations, is tasked with restructuring the arrangements between Canada and its First Peoples. This is the work of reconciliation—recognizing and implementing the rights of Indigenous Peoples. This includes the right to self-determination, including self-government.

In the meantime, while the relationships minister gets on with the work of reconciliation, and until such time as Indigenous Peoples can fully exercise self-determination, the federal government has an obligation to continue the service-delivery role it took on for itself, as described in Section 91(24) of the Constitution Act of 1867. Our new department, called Indigenous Services Canada, was charged with improving those services. This is an enormous task, and it affects the realities of daily life for First Nations, Inuit, and Métis Peoples.

The deputy minister assigned to the new department was Jean-François Tremblay. The two of us, with our teams, knew we should start by listening to representatives of the distinct groups of Indigenous Peoples—First Nations, Inuit, and Métis—about what should be prioritized. As a result, we decided to settle on five top files: child welfare, health, infrastructure (including clean drinking water), education, and economic development. The child welfare file would turn out to be the place of my most intense focus.

My first official trip in this new role was to Winnipeg, Manitoba, where I heard Cora Morgan and others describe their most urgent concerns. I had arrived in Winnipeg that chilly Tuesday morning, and we went straight from the airport to meet with the AMC at their headquarters in a tall, narrow tower at the corner of Portage and Smith. The AMC Grand Chief at the time was Arlen Dumas. My official business was to announce that the federal government was giving them $800,000 to support the FNFAO. My team had prepared a speech for me to deliver. More important, the leaders of the AMC and the FNFAO had stories for me.

What I learned from Cora Morgan and others that day set the stage for one of the most important laws I helped to draft, one that would affirm the rights and jurisdiction of Indigenous Peoples in the matter of child welfare. That meeting was the motivation for our work. Its revelations sent me and key members of my team on a mission we would pursue with unrelenting commitment over the next eighteen months. We began to examine what the federal government could do quickly to reverse the damaging policies and practices that were tearing families apart.

In addition to sharing that a child was taken from its family every day, usually at birth, they told me there were about eleven thousand children in the child welfare system in the province of Manitoba, and over 90 percent of them were Indigenous. They proceeded to describe something I had never heard about before—a practice called "birth alerts," whereby a flag was marked on the medical record of a woman about to give birth. It was a signal to the hospital system that Child and Family Services (CFS) should be notified when the baby was born. In most cases, it was an indicator that the baby would be apprehended from its family.

It is shocking that this happens in Canada in the twenty-first century. The concept of birth alerts reminded me of Nathaniel Hawthorne's *The Scarlet Letter*, a novel set in the seventeenth-century, in which a woman was forced to wear a mark for life, for the purpose of public humiliation, as penance for giving birth to a child with unknown paternity. The birth alert was not a mark that a woman would wear, but it was a mark in her medical files, and it was as devastating as a scarlet letter.

I asked many questions that day and in the months that followed to understand more about this practice and its implications. I learned that a woman could be marked with a birth alert for several reasons including, but not limited to, being a minor; having grown up as a child in care; having had a previous child apprehended; having (or the baby's father having) a substance-use disorder; living in inadequate housing; and, apparently, even for the alleged sin of living in poverty. There seemed to be no requirement that the woman would be informed about this flag on her health record. The real-life stories about this practice helped me to understand its impact. Cora Morgan told me about a young Cree woman whom I will call Janette.

Janette was near the end of her fourth pregnancy when she contacted the FNFAO with a simple hope: "When my baby is born, I just want to spend twenty-four hours with him or her."

The background to that request was distressing but apparently not unusual. Janette had been a child in care herself—the first mark against her in the birth alert system. When I met Janette months later, she told me in some detail about leaving her foster home at the age of sixteen with all her life's material possessions in a green garbage bag. Before long, she was pregnant with her first child. In addition to having been a child in care herself, she was an "underage" mother—another trigger for a birth alert. Indeed, when the baby was born in Winnipeg General Hospital, the care team notified CFS, whose agent apprehended the infant immediately.

The second baby was born when Janette was an adult, but she now had another cause for a birth alert; that is, she had a previous child taken into care. This was apparently an indicator that she might not be fit to parent, so the second baby was taken as well. The third baby was apprehended for similar reasons. Janette tried in vain to fight it, but by this time, the system had enough evidence to prove to its satisfaction that she would not be able to care for the child.

By the time of her fourth pregnancy, she knew what would happen. There was nothing she wanted more than to be a mother, to pour her love into a little child and to enjoy its love in return. Thankfully, she learned about Cora Morgan and the FNFAO. The pregnancy was well advanced by the time she made the connection and shared her simple hope to have just one full day to bond with her newborn.

Cora and the team did what they could, but with little time to intervene, they were unsuccessful in their initial efforts. Janette did not get those precious first twenty-four hours with her baby. It was apprehended from her immediately after birth.

I listened with astonishment to this story on that autumn day in Winnipeg. I knew enough about what keeps mothers and babies well to be extremely concerned about how "the system" was systematically pulling families apart.

When a young woman is so determined to be a mother that she tries time and again to be one, but our public institutions wrench those babies from her, there is something seriously wrong. Did the child welfare agency try everything possible to support her as a mother before taking her children away? I had to find out more.

Entire books should and will be written about the twenty-first-century baby scoop that rips apart thousands of families, almost all of them Indigenous or otherwise racialized. When I understood what was happening on our watch, I was shaken. I was ashamed. I also had a solemn duty to respond because I was in a position to do something about these harmful practices. As a result, I became completely preoccupied with finding solutions.

Two weeks after that meeting in Winnipeg, the PM requested a "take stock" meeting with my team and me to hear our early advice about what our focus should be in the new Department of Indigenous Services Canada. He was heavily focused on how we were going to eliminate all long-term drinking water advisories for First Nations on reserve. Our team had an entire, meticulous plan underway to address that, and I shared his conviction about its importance.

I took the opportunity to highlight for him this other issue, the massive over-apprehension of Indigenous children into the child welfare system. I told him the story of Janette. It hit hard. He was across a big table from me, but not so far away that I could not see the authentic tears welling up in his eyes. He asked what we could do.

Senator Murray Sinclair, a First Nations lawyer and former judge who chaired the Truth and Reconciliation Commission (TRC), was also at the table that day. In 2015, the commission had put forth ninety-four Calls to Action and, in the same year, the PM promised that the new government would "completely implement" those calls.

I knew that many of those Calls to Action were in my portfolio, and one specifically related to the crisis I had brought to the PM's attention. I looked over at Senator Sinclair as I advised the PM that we should do exactly what the TRC Call to Action Number 4 had outlined. It says:

> We call upon the federal government to enact Aboriginal **child-welfare legislation** that establishes national standards for Aboriginal child apprehension and custody cases and includes principles that:

i. Affirm the right of Aboriginal governments to establish and maintain their own child-welfare agencies.

ii. Require all child-welfare agencies and courts to take the residential school legacy into account in their decision making.

iii. Establish, as an important priority, a requirement that placements of Aboriginal children into temporary and permanent care be culturally appropriate [emphasis added].[2]

The PM asked Senator Sinclair to weigh in. In his thoughtful, unhurried commentary, the senator reminded us it was not by coincidence that the first five Calls to Action of the TRC were related to child welfare. Pay attention, he was telling us. They are in that order for a reason. They were and are our top-priority calls.

The senator's message was clear: Get to work. With that and the PM's concurrence, I had the mandate and affirmation I needed to co-develop a response to the crisis in Indigenous child welfare. The concept of co-development was new, and was one of the keys if we were to achieve anything on this file. It meant that the federal government would work in partnership and collaboration with Indigenous leaders to develop a comprehensive response.

In the following days, facing a scrum of journalists, I described the over-apprehension of Indigenous children, and spontaneously called the situation "a humanitarian crisis." After my encounter with press, I fretted about whether I had been overly dramatic. But many Indigenous leaders later thanked me for raising the alarm with those words. They repeated that phrase and seized the opening we had provided for their gut-wrenching stories to be more widely heard.

My chief of staff was enthusiastic about our new portfolio and used his imagination to get things done.[3] He came up with the idea that we should call an emergency meeting about child welfare, bringing Indigenous leaders together with provincial and territorial ministers and officials. The invitations went out just three weeks after the pivotal meeting in Winnipeg.

While there was initial skepticism about who would attend, hundreds would eventually show up for the two-day session at the end of January 2018. Indigenous political leaders were joined by Elders and grandmothers, as well as young people who had grown up in foster care. There were representatives of federal, provincial, and territorial governments, as well as social services agencies. The meeting was not just for show. We were serious about interrupting long-standing patterns of injustice, and we needed buy-in from all orders of government and civil society. Though it wasn't our top goal, we were happy that the media paid attention too. This helped to accelerate our work.

Over the next year, our team in Indigenous Services tackled the issue from as many angles as possible, listening to as many voices as possible. It was the period of greatest learning during my time in government. My teachers were largely Indigenous. They included renowned experts such as the invincible Cindy Blackstock, who is a national hero. She is best known for her exceptional work to bring the issue of Indigenous child welfare to the Canadian Human Rights Tribunal. It's fair to say that governments do not always like being called to account for their actions in the tireless manner that Cindy has modelled, but her advocacy on behalf of children has been highly effective and unparalleled.

I also learned from countless mothers, grandparents, and youth whose families had been taken apart by the child welfare system. One woman Elder told me that what children need to thrive is four L's—their land, their language, their lineage, and their loved ones. These are their sources of belonging, at the core of their cultural identity, and the centre of their well-being. These are the elements of nurture that children lose when they are apprehended from their families.

Several chiefs of First Nations were highly effective in describing not only how the families were being taken apart, but also how they wanted to implement their own laws and practices to ensure the well-being of their children. One of those was then Kúkpi7 (Chief) Wenecwtsin (Wayne Christian), who is of Secwépemc and Syilx Okanagan ancestry. When we visited the British Columbia community of Splatsin First Nation in October 2018, he hosted a ceremony for our team—complete with feasting and traditional dance. He explained that this was to bless me, as a federal minister, in my work on child welfare. He sent me back to Ottawa with symbolic gifts, including colourful bundles of ribbons, to represent the children who were counting on me to persevere in amending the laws, policies, and practices regarding Indigenous child welfare.

Our plan to respond to the crisis was multipronged. It included new funding for children with disabilities, so they could remain with their families. The largest commitment of funding was used to implement Jordan's Principle—named in memory of Jordan River Anderson, a boy from Norway House Cree Nation in Manitoba. He was born with severe disabilities and never had access to the care he needed to go home from the hospital because the federal and provincial governments battled for years about who was responsible for the costs of his home-based care. He died in hospital at age five and had never been to his home.

We were determined that no child should be denied care for their disabilities or kept apart from their family because of a jurisdictional dispute. The federal government made the investments to live up to this principle, and more than three million unique supports and services have been provided for First Nations children since the funding started in 2016.[4]

But the most ambitious piece of work was the co-creation of a new federal law: An Act respecting First Nations, Inuit, and Métis children, youth, and families. I was not alone in these efforts. To co-write the law, we had a working group of First Nations, Inuit, and Métis leaders and their advisors, along with federal bureaucrats and political staff. They considered all the elements that should be included in the legislation, while we sought the advice of as many communities and individuals as possible to design and draft legislation in approximately six months—the kind of speed we believed was warranted given the humanitarian crisis. It was no small task to navigate all the perspectives, the personalities, and the politics to put together Bill C-92. In the end, the legislation may not have incorporated all the input we received—few laws can boast that—but its strength and effectiveness has been demonstrated.

The basis of the new law was this: Indigenous people have well-established rights. Obviously, they have human rights.

They also have inherent rights as First Peoples. They have treaty rights, based on the historic agreements made with Canada in good faith. Their rights are recognized in international documents such as the United Nations Declaration on the Rights of Indigenous Peoples (UNDRIP). Their rights are documented in Canada's constitution. Section 35 of the 1982 Constitution Act affirms the Rights of Aboriginal Peoples of Canada. That section stands parallel to our esteemed Charter of Rights and Freedoms. It should receive the same solemn respect that is appropriately ascribed to the Charter, yet Section 35 of our constitution has often been conveniently forgotten, until the courts have been required to weigh in and remind everyone.

Those rights of Indigenous Peoples include the right to self-determination. The UNDRIP notes "the right to autonomy or self-government in matters relating to their internal and local affairs,"[5] as well as the particular entitlement of Indigenous "families and communities to retain shared responsibility for the upbringing, training, education and well-being of their children."[6]

Bill C-92 passed into law in 2019. It did not confer any new rights on Indigenous Peoples. Those rights were pre-existing, as mentioned above. But the new legislation made it clear that Indigenous governments could exert jurisdiction in relation to child and family services. Since then, the Government of Quebec has challenged the constitutionality of the bill. The Quebec Court of Appeal upheld the majority of the act, including the right of Indigenous Peoples in Canada to exercise jurisdiction over child and family services, but struck out provisions that Indigenous laws would prevail in the event of a conflict with a provincial law. For a definitive response to that issue, it has been referred to the Supreme Court of Canada. The Bill C-92 Reference case was heard there in December 2022, but at the time of writing, the court's highly anticipated decision has not yet been announced.

In the meantime, Cowessess First Nation in Saskatchewan was one of the first communities in the country to re-exert jurisdiction for child welfare, starting in 2021, emboldened by the federal law derived from Bill C-92. Their elected leader, Chief Cadmus Delorme, invited me to a virtual gathering of other First Nations leaders in June 2022, so I could hear how they were developing their own child welfare laws. At that time, five First Nations communities had passed their own Child and Family Services laws. As of July 2023, another forty-four communities had notified the federal government of their intention to do the same.[7]

In addition to recognizing the right to self-determination, Bill C-92 has demonstrated its benefit by establishing the minimum standards for how CFS services must be provided for Indigenous children. This includes a provision in the law that children cannot be apprehended solely on the basis of their socio-economic conditions. I always thought it was absurd, not to mention discriminatory, that children were taken from their families on the basis of poverty, and then foster families were paid thousands of dollars per month to care for these same children.

Finally, based on the establishment of those minimum standards, I'm happy to report that across the country, one by one, provinces are changing their policies and declaring that birth alerts are no longer allowed.

I reconnected with Cora Morgan when I was writing this book, to confirm some details about the work we did together. She said I should not under-emphasize the magnitude of the change that was made by Bill C-92. By email, she wrote: "On the ground, it really empowered families and Nations. It truly caused CFS agencies to second guess the status quo, which helped families in real ways. Think of the significance of a child staying home or going home instead of being placed in a stranger's home."

What gives me the greatest joy is to hear about families who have been reunited. This is not directly attributable to the law I helped to write, but I believe our work played a role in bringing the country's attention to the harms that we have allowed to perpetuate.

As for Janette, she was reunited with her four children, and I had the pleasure of seeing them together. Despite the positive outcome, her story is a dreadful reminder that certain laws, policies, and practices of our country have resulted in indescribable trauma and harm for Indigenous Peoples. It is also an example of how one invincible woman, like Janette, with the help of people like Cora, can fight the system and bring her children home.

What I have written here offers merely a snapshot of the very large volume of issues wherein the survival, dignity, and well-being of Indigenous Peoples requires a rights-based reform of Canadian laws, policies, and practices. I hope it is sufficient to demonstrate that in the overall pursuit of wellness, and from the specific lens of social systems, there is a distinct body of work to be done based on respecting the rights of First Nations, Inuit, and Métis Peoples. We've only just begun.

I've referred thus far to the role of policy-makers as it relates to the well-being of our country, our communities, and ourselves. In most cases, the people I'm referring to are our political leaders. It should be clear by now that the ability to be a country with health for all requires societal governance with that goal in mind. A healthy country needs a foundation of healthy politics. That's where we turn our attention next. The political determinants of health may be the most critical of all, and the hardest to manoeuvre.

PART FOUR

Political

CHAPTER 11

Nothing But Medicine Writ Large

I never viewed the transition in my career from medicine to politics as a change of direction or vocation. The links between the two have been widely understood for centuries. In fact, if you ask any doctor who has an interest in public policy about the connection, they will likely point you to a quote from nineteenth-century German physician-politician-philosopher Rudolf Virchow, who said that "Medicine is a social science and politics is nothing else but medicine on a large scale. Medicine as a social science, as the science of human beings, has the obligation to point out problems and to attempt their theoretical solution; the politician, the practical anthropologist, must find the means for their actual solution."[1]

Politics is nothing but medicine writ large. It's the leap from healing individuals to healing society. Politicians set the societal rules that have a profound impact on who will be well. For me, the move to politics was simply a way to improve people's health on a grander scale. This is why I always encourage health professionals to be open to a career in politics.

The instruments are different, but the end goal is the same. It's all about the well-being of people and populations.

It was former prime minister Paul Martin who lit the spark in me to get involved in politics. Years before I met him, I had started a campaign called Give a Day for World AIDS, to raise money for people living with HIV. Donations were directed to the Stephen Lewis Foundation and Dignitas International. In our efforts to raise awareness, we recruited high-profile speakers who would draw a crowd. In November 2010, we felt very lucky to secure both humanitarian physician Dr. James Orbinski and the Right Honourable Paul Martin, Canada's twenty-first prime minister, to speak at a breakfast event for prospective donors.

The formal program was to start at 8 a.m., but Mr. Martin agreed to arrive an hour early and meet me in a lounge near the hall for the main event. He was over seventy at the time and full of energy as he greeted me, immediately putting me at ease despite my nervous anticipation about meeting with him.

We chatted about Canada's role in the world, and he told me about his efforts to promote business development in sub-Saharan Africa. I talked about how Canada could be more effective in its foreign aid if it invested not just in elementary school education but also at the post-secondary level. I told him about my work with the Toronto Addis Ababa Academic Collaboration and asked for advice about how we might seek government funding or philanthropy for the program.

As we were chatting, I expressed my frustration about Canada's foreign policy in the area of official development assistance. Somehow during the conversation, as I was becoming more impassioned about the subject at hand, I said,

"Sometimes I think I should just run for office so I could have a voice in Ottawa and see what I could do to fix things."

He interrupted me with a question: "Did you just say you're thinking of going into politics?"

"Ha!" I responded. "I wasn't serious. That would be non-sensical. I have four kids. I have a job that I love, as a family doctor . . ."

"No, no, no," he interrupted again. "You should really think about this. If you join a political party, you'd better join the Liberals," he said, as an aside. "If you can get yourself nominated as a candidate; if you can get elected; if your party forms government; and if, someday, you can get yourself around a cabinet table, then you could accomplish more in ten minutes for the causes that are important to you than you can accomplish in ten years of your advocacy work outside government."

I had never joined a political party, in large part because of my work at the hospital and the university. I wanted to be able to advocate for health-related causes without having a partisan affiliation. The truth is, I had interest in a range of parties and their platforms.

It was my interest in global health and geopolitics that directed my attention to federal politics in mid-life. I was furious at Conservative leader Stephen Harper before he was PM, when he said he would have supported Canada's participation in the war in Iraq. After he became prime minister, there were policies of his government I found particularly vexing, as a family doctor committed to social justice. This included their efforts to eliminate access to health care for refugees, which seemed not only cruel but unwise from a public health and public policy perspective.

In the lead-up to the 2011 federal election, I was paying more attention than usual—with Paul Martin's words ringing in my head. Watching the interaction during one of the leaders' debates, I was not impressed with the tone and substance of the discourse—though the New Democratic Party leader, the late Jack Layton, was the most reasonable. It turned out to be a pivotal election, as the Liberals were trounced under then leader Michael Ignatieff. Stephen Harper won a large majority government. This did not please me. I decided it was time for me to get involved.

The day after the election, during a lunch break at my clinic, I went online to review the media coverage. I watched Mr. Ignatieff's concession speech and wondered what would become of the Liberal Party after this resounding defeat. I also wondered what new opportunities might present themselves as the party rebuilt. It was time to find out. Then and there, at age fifty, I did something for the first time in my life: I joined a political party.

I was not sure where my new-found partisan affiliation would lead, but I was curious and ready to roll up my sleeves, to help shape the political future of my country.

Luckily for me, the local riding association had a devoted and diligent president, Bill Attwell, who got me involved right away. He had received an email notification that I had become a member. Bill was a high school teacher, and he recognized my name from my work in the community; he called me up shortly after and invited me to meet for coffee. The local Liberals had lost the seat for the second time in a row, each time to Conservative Paul Calandra. Bill seemed thrilled that in spite of the party's historic loss, someone was ready to join the riding association. He told me about the group and encouraged me to attend the next meeting. The next four years would turn out to be an energizing experience of learning the ropes of politics at the local level. I volunteered to be the policy lead for the riding association and learned how community members can provide input to party platforms. As time went on, it became clear to me and to others that I should seek a nomination to run in the next election as the federal Liberal candidate in my riding.

I look back now on those years and think about how outlandish it was for me to get involved in politics at that point in time. As I had told Paul Martin, I was a mother of four. I had a large roster of patients as a family doctor. I was chief of the Department of Family Medicine at Markham Stouffville Hospital, and we had just launched a new academic FHT and a new Family Medicine Teaching Unit as an expansion site of the University of Toronto. I was still finishing up the final courses for a master of public health, and still running the Give a Day to World AIDS campaign. To top it off, my colleagues and I were in the final stages of supporting the launch of the first ever family medicine residency training program at Addis Ababa University in Ethiopia, and I was travelling there twice a year to work on that. The truth is, I loved those years so much. All the activity that led to the election captivated me and gave me hope.

After I started attending activities with the local riding association, I met some of the regional party organizers. Early in 2013, I was contacted by Gary Anandasangaree, who asked if I would help co-chair a local team in support of Justin Trudeau in his bid to become party leader.

I was honoured to be asked but wanted some due diligence. I told Gary I would be open to helping, but before I threw my name behind Justin Trudeau, I would appreciate a chance to meet the man, to decide for myself if he would be a good leader, if I should lend him the support of my name and work on his behalf. Gary assured me that someone would arrange that, but in the meantime, they were getting their teams set up and he hoped I would agree to help right away.

So, without having met the candidate, I accepted a role as co-chair of Justin Trudeau's leadership campaign at the level of the local riding association and looked for ways to help. I knew one of the biggest needs would be fundraising, and I've learned a fair bit about raising money over the years, thanks to my occupation and a personal network of people with discretionary income. I've also learned how to work with a team to throw a superb party.

My first project to support Mr. Trudeau's leadership was probably the move that brought his team's attention to a previously unknown family doctor in Markham-Stouffville. I told the folks running his campaign that I would plan a cocktail party and raise $40,000. I was an unknown, but they probably figured they didn't have much to lose, so they assigned me a date. No one but me knows how hard I worked to sell those tickets. In less than a month, we sold more than eighty of them at $500 each, and we hosted the future prime minister at an elegant reception on March 26, 2013, where I met Mr. Trudeau for the first time and introduced him to some influential people from our community.

I'm proud of the fact that I found a way into politics on my own terms. When I was eventually nominated as the Liberal candidate, it was because I followed the steps of the democratic process. I was not recruited by the party. I was not identified by political operatives as a star candidate and parachuted into the riding. This was my home turf. I was qualified to represent what would be a new riding called Markham-Stouffville because I lived there, I was a family doctor there, and we raised our family there. I already knew a lot about the views of community members, and I was prepared to keep listening if elected to represent them.

I received some good advice from Hari Subramaniam, who was married to one of my medical colleagues and had worked on a few campaigns. He made a smart suggestion that I've never heard from anyone else. He said, "Start a list. Write down the names of everyone you know in your riding. Keep writing until you have at least a thousand names. Then invite every one of them to join the party to support your nomination." I did exactly that. Between my colleagues, our church, our kids' schools and sports teams, and our neighbourhood, I knew a lot of people.

It was time for a coming-out party. But first, I needed to tell my patients about my plans by sending a letter to each one. Then I told my community. On September 12, 2013, I posted this on my personal website.

> *I came out of the closet this week about my political*
> *aspirations. I sent an email to my medical colleagues*
> *informing them that I would be stepping down next summer*
> *as Chief of the Department of Family Medicine at our hospital*
> *in order to have time to prepare a campaign. I will be seeking*
> *a nomination with the Liberal Party of Canada with the*

objective of being a candidate in the next federal election. It was a little difficult to click "send" on those emails. I was exposing my dreams more publicly than ever before. I felt excited, hopeful, and nervous all at the same time.

As "coming out of the closet" goes, I understand that the revelation of my political goals was much less shocking and risky than it would be to step out of many other kinds of closets in which people find security. Nonetheless it has taken some courage (and a small measure of madness perhaps) to formalize this decision that I've been considering for several years now.

The reaction from colleagues has been overwhelmingly positive. I received so many kind words and offers of help. A few people have expressed trepidation. A non-medical friend wrote about her initial feelings of surprise: "Why would you put yourself through the travail of politics when you are already such a significant influence in your chosen field at home and abroad? And why would you subject yourself to the abuse and public scrutiny that politicians have to endure in political life?" The same person went on to write a kind letter of encouragement. But her questions made me reflect on why I would make such a career decision.

Why would I leave medicine and enter politics? I've hinted before that it's not such a stretch. I became a physician so I could devote myself to helping individuals and their families to have healthy and meaningful lives. Over the years I have observed how greatly the health of individuals and families is affected by the health of the community. As a result, I have become engaged in politics with the goal of helping to build a healthier society.

—

On April 9, 2014, I was formally declared a candidate with the Liberal Party of Canada, and we began actively preparing for an election that was still eighteen months away. On that date, my speech included this line, which captured my motivation, and to which I have since clung: "For me, a seat in the House of Commons is not a target, it's a tool. It's the tool that you and I will use to make this community better—to make this country better."

The energy associated with the broader 2015 federal election campaign was more than my imagination. It was palpable. Stephen Harper had been prime minister for nine years, and the Canadian public was ready for new leadership. Justin Trudeau and the team took advantage of that, campaigning on a slogan of "real change." The Liberal Party was in third place in terms of seats in the House of Commons, so it was truly a long shot to suppose that the party could go from there to a majority government. Yet that's exactly what happened. I was one of 338 Liberal candidates across the country. Our teams were dizzy with enthusiasm. The recipe of "hope and hard work" was an apt description of how we operated.

Mr. Trudeau made one visit to my riding that year. It was before the official campaign had even been started. He was in big demand, but we managed to get on his schedule to visit downtown Stouffville the evening of June 18, when the town was having one its favourite regular events—a Food Truck Frenzy. They were shutting down Main Street right in front of my campaign office.

The crowd on Main Street that day was about two thousand strong. And the word *frenzy* was a fitting way to capture the sentiment of the crowd that was motivated in part by the line-ups to get sausage dogs, poutine, BeaverTails, or whatever else the food trucks were offering. The smell emanating from hot oil in the trucks' deep fryers filled the air. Music was pumping out from the speakers operated by the crew from Stouffville's own WhiStle Radio. Word was out that Justin Trudeau was coming to town, and you'd better have your cell phone ready if you were hoping for a selfie.

Just as the leader and his entourage drove into town and I was set to connect with them at the local commuter train station, the skies opened up and poured down buckets of rain. There were few umbrellas to be found, so as Justin Trudeau emerged from his car, we had a rapid greeting and then made a mad dash to the back door entrance of our campaign office to escape the torrent, hoping the rain would soon settle enough to go out and greet whoever remained in the crowds.

I laugh at myself as I recall that I had gone out to get my hair done that afternoon so I would look my best when I greeted the Liberal Party leader. It was a good lesson in limiting my vanity that I had to go through the rest of that visit, including all the pictures that were taken, with my rain-soaked mop of hair. Politics is supposed to be about how you think, not how you look. On that memorable afternoon, Mother Nature made sure I understood that truth.

About four months after Justin Trudeau visited my riding, after eighteen months of meticulously organized campaign-ing, on October 19, 2015, election day arrived. Both our local team in Markham-Stouffville and the national Liberal cam-paign were met with success. It was a Liberal majority govern-ment. In our riding, by a margin of about four thousand votes,

I defeated the Conservative incumbent. I was a political outsider with a determination to learn the ropes so I could use my new position to promote a healthier society. Two weeks later, I would be sworn in as minister of health. I could never have predicted all the joys and challenges that lay ahead.

CHAPTER 12

When Politics Works

Candice was one of the most kind-hearted patients I ever knew. She was a frequent visitor in our Markham clinic, and people were charmed by her. She got to know the receptionists and other members of the team and called them by name. She would compliment them on their outfits and ask about their day. She arrived in the waiting room with the presence of someone who had stepped onto a stage. Other patients would look up from their seats, watch her with curiosity, and then slowly start to smile. Usually, she had an appointment when she showed up. But if she didn't have one, it would be hard to say no to her polite request to have "just a minute of Dr. Philpott's time" for a quick question.

Much less often, Candice would show up with a different demeanour. She was never rude and never ungrateful, but the joy was gone. She wore dark glasses and a long-sleeved shirt, with her long, brown hair more tangled than usual. She would be much quieter in the waiting room, and it was only in the privacy of the examination room that she would tell me what had happened.

Candice was beautiful—inside and out. She was brilliant. She was writing a book about her life, and I wonder if she ever finished it. Her life was troubled and complicated. She had experienced far more than her share of trauma, including the death of her only two children, in an accident that left her with both grief and chronic pain. She had been repeatedly abused by men in her life. They took advantage of her need for housing, which made it hard for her to walk away.

Candice became dependent on opioids as the only way to get temporary relief from both physical and psychological pain. I tried to help her with both. I made referrals to social services and called them regularly to compare notes on how we could be helpful, on keeping her safe. I struggled with every decision about what to prescribe for her—not wanting to exacerbate her substance dependence but knowing that if she didn't get clean medications from me, she would use unregulated drugs that could be laced with unspecified amounts of toxic products that could kill her. I wanted her to stay alive. Both of us believed she had a brighter future ahead.

I'm not sure how much I was able to help her over the years that I was her doctor, but I know she educated me. She helped me understand why someone would regularly use substances. I saw how our social structures failed to provide her with the security she needed to live and work with safety and stability. Through those lessons, Candice and several other patients helped me bring both humanity and reality to the topic of Canada's drug laws and policies.

The health minister's suite is on the sixteenth floor of the Brooke Claxton Building, an edifice that some people mockingly referred to as the "Black Tower of Power." It's one of the buildings the government plans to dispose of in the years ahead. From the windows of the minister's office, you have a magnificent view of the Ottawa River and Parliament Hill. Inside the room, I had a large oval table with space for at least a dozen people to be seated.

I spent hundreds of hours around that table being briefed by public servants and advised by political staff. Every week was a marathon of decision-making, and I loved every minute of it.

It's fair to say the public servants were happy to have a medical doctor in this portfolio for the first time in Canada's history. They could often skip past the first half of the briefing documents because I already understood the bioscience and policy landscape for many of the issues we had to address. The briefing package about tuberculosis, for example, had been developed to start with "What is a mycobacterium?" We were quickly able to get past all that.

In many cases, I could tell that the public service was bringing me policy work they had been developing for years, just waiting for someone who would come along and say, yes, let's do it.

An obvious example of that was in our work on drugs and substances. I could use what I had learned from patients such as Candice to develop laws and policies that could help someone like her. Here was an area where I could save lives with the stroke of a pen. In 2015, when I came to office, a person still required a prescription to get access to naloxone, a drug that could be injected to reverse the effects of an opioid overdose, thereby potentially saving someone's life. In my first official decision as minister, I changed those rules, enabling naloxone to be widely available in pharmacies across the country in multiple formats. Looking back, it's shocking to recall that such an important life-saving treatment was so inaccessible. With that decision, Paul Martin's prediction came true: you could sometimes accomplish more in ten minutes as a cabinet minister than you might in ten years as an advocate on the outside of government.

This was the first in a long series of decisions I made that would impact the lives of people who use drugs. Whatever my achievements were in the health portfolio, the progress we made on drug policy was some of the most meaningful work to me. I only regret that I was not there long enough to do more.

If you were to ask most Canadians what was the most important change in drug laws enacted by the forty-second Parliament, they would tell you about our work to legalize and regulate access to cannabis. That was a well-known part of the 2015 Liberal election platform, so as minister of health, I knew it would be part of my job to make good on that campaign promise. That work was assigned to three ministers: me, as minister of health; the minister for public safety, Ralph Goodale; and the minister of justice and attorney general, Jody Wilson-Raybould.

I'm proud of the work we did on the cannabis file. It was not necessarily my favourite initiative, but I knew it was important and I believed wholeheartedly in the wisdom of the legal changes we undertook. I have never used cannabis myself and have no plans to do so. Neither do I desire to promote the use of cannabis. There are legitimate concerns about its impact on the overall well-being of some users. Even so, I firmly believe that its use should not be criminalized.

The decriminalization of cannabis is one of those public policy matters that gets misunderstood and manipulated for political ends. There are many lifestyle decisions adults make that are risky or unhealthy—the use of alcohol included. The use of tobacco is clearly unhealthy as well, but there is no evidence that criminalizing the use of these products decreases the risks to population health.

On the contrary, the criminalization of substance use leads to enormous harms for people and populations. From a financial perspective alone, the costs associated with criminalization are more than $10 billion annually for policing, courts, and correctional services.[1] More important, the criminal prohibition of drug use prevents people from seeking treatment, for fear of arrest. It perpetuates the illicit drug market, with its contaminated products, and hence exacerbates the potential harms of drug use. Additionally, we know that smart public health measures that maximize public education and improve access to care are more effective in reducing drug-related harms.[2]

Thus, we chose to emphasize the health rationale for our work to develop the Cannabis Act, and I became the public face of this work. To some people's amusement, we formally announced our plans on April 20, 2016. You probably know that 4/20 is an annual date affectionately known by some as Weed Day. I had the honour of making that historic announcement to the world at the United Nations General Assembly Special Session on the World Drug Problem.

Standing in front of that iconic dark green marble wall in the General Assembly Hall at UN Headquarters in New York City, I started my speech by talking about a mother whose daughter had died from complications of substance use. Then

I began to talk about work we were doing in Canada. In that hall of international leaders, I described my support for Insite, the supervised consumption site in Vancouver. As I made that reference, there were outbursts of applause from the crowd of activists gathered in the balcony. Then I began to talk about access to naloxone and other measures of harm reduction. I went on to announce:

> In Canada we will apply these principles with regard to marijuana. To that end we will introduce legislation in the spring of 2017 that ensures that we keep marijuana out of the hands of children and profits out of the hands of criminals. While this plan challenges the status quo in many countries, we are convinced it is the best way to protect our youth while enhancing public safety. Canada will continue to modernize our approach to drug policy. . . . Our work will embrace upstream prevention, compassionate treatment, and harm reduction. We will work with law enforcement partners to encourage appropriate and proportionate criminal justice measures. We know it is impossible to arrest our way out of this problem. . . . I believe that—if we respect one another's perspectives and seek common ground— we can achieve our shared objective: protecting our citizens. Better yet, we can improve their lives.

For people who had spent decades advocating for compassionate and evidence-informed drug policy, it was a pivotal moment, a key signal that with enough political will, we could make inroads toward ending the global war on drugs.

A comprehensive approach was required to pull off the Cannabis Act. I give credit to the entire team across the portfolios of health, public safety, and justice. The Prime Minister's Office (PMO) took great interest in this file. Gerald Butts, then principal secretary to the PM, pushed hard on the timeline, pressing for the legislation to be tabled by the spring of 2017 so legalization would be a reality by the end of our term in 2019. We asked a former politician, the Honourable Anne McLellan, to lead a consultation task force. The team in my minister's office met with hundreds of MPs and senators of all parties to make sure every parliamentary voice could be heard. We met the target. At the summer solstice, June 21, 2017, the Cannabis Act received royal assent. We spent the following two years working on the accompanying regulatory changes. It was a monumental piece of work in the long saga of evolving international drug laws.

During this time, I was also working on other drug policy matters that were even more important—to me and to the people who would be affected by the reform of laws and policies. When we formed the government, the country was waking up to a public health emergency that was receiving inadequate attention. Across the country, thousands of people were dying of opioid-related overdoses. To our shame, no one in the country had accurate and timely data about how many people were dying, and there was no national strategy for how to prevent these deaths. From data that were acquired later, we know that in 2016 on average, there were eight opioid-related deaths and sixteen opioid-related hospitalizations every day across Canada. Tragically, those numbers have continued to rise. In 2022, on average, more than twenty people died every day from opioid toxicity.

Under the previous government, the Controlled Drugs and Substances Act had been amended to remove harm reduction as a pillar of the national response. I was determined to reverse that. It was part of a huge task to overturn the impact of the decades-long international war on drugs. People were literally dying on our watch, and some of those deaths were preventable. I knew we had to make progress. Within the first year we had put in place a federal action plan to reduce harms associated with opioids and had taken action to save lives.

After authorizing naloxone for non-prescription use and making it available in multiple formats, the next task was to improve access to other harm-reduction services. There were only two supervised consumption sites serving the public. Each was operating under an injunction and was at risk of being shut down.

Within three months of my appointment as minister of health, my political team suggested I make a point by visiting Insite, Canada's first and best-known supervised consumption site. They didn't need to twist my arm. Every step of the way, our work was informed by listening to people who use drugs, to their families, and to those who provided care for people who use drugs. This visit was no exception.

I had never visited such a facility before, and I was highly attuned to sending the right message. I knew my visit would send a positive signal to harm-reduction advocates that our government was serious about reforming drug policy. But I did not want my visit to further stigmatize or dehumanize the clients of Insite. Most of all, I did not want to indulge in sensationalism in any way. I wanted it to be low-key.

I was warmly welcomed by the Insite staff, who recognized me as an ally in their harm-reduction work. After a brief conversation outside, we moved into the foyer, and they gave me an overview of the impressive multi-purpose facility. Then we moved further inside, to the main room used for consuming drugs by injection. It was clean, quiet, and unadorned. The ambiance simultaneously evoked the feel of a clinic but also of a place where people would feel at home.

I tried not to stare at anyone, but I did look at the face of each person sitting at a station. Each of these stations was equipped with a chair, a stainless-steel countertop, and a mirror. I wished I could know each person's story. I thought of former patients like Candice, who'd never had access to a place like this. I wept with both relief and sadness. The relief came from knowing there was a place where people could quietly and safely inject substances under supervision, so that if the drugs they brought with them included fentanyl or other potent agents, and if the drug caused enough respiratory suppression to stop their breathing, someone would administer naloxone to keep them alive. If the clients were ready and interested, they could also access detox and treatment services as needed.

My tears of sadness are harder to explain. They came from realizing that, as crucial as supervised injection sites are to saving lives, they are not the only answer to this deadly crisis. I suspect that none of those individuals grew up dreaming of a future that included being a client at Insite. I wondered about the trauma that had brought them to this place, and about what awaited them in the days ahead. They would stay alive for now, but they were dependent on drug use. The only way to get those drugs was through illicit and unsafe supply chains. Insite was only part of what they needed for wellness.

As an initial step, we gave a four-year exemption to both Insite and the Dr. Peter Centre in Vancouver, so they were approved to continue operations. We began working with other groups across the country who wanted to operate a supervised consumption site. This ranged from private clinics to provincial health authorities. After listening to advocates, activists, and legal advisors, it became clear that a new law was required to formally reintroduce harm reduction as a pillar of federal drug policy and to simplify and streamline the application process for communities that want and need to establish supervised consumption sites. In the spring of 2017, Bill C-37 did just that. The new rules replaced the onerous burden of meeting twenty-six criteria in the application process with only meeting the bar of the five key factors outlined in the Supreme Court of Canada 2011 decision regarding Insite, thus facilitating approvals for new harm-reduction services across the country. As of 2023, there were thirty-eight sites serving Canadians, with an estimated 2,600 visits per day.[3] The staff at these sites attended to about 47,000 overdoses and drug-related medical emergencies over the first six years after the law passed, with no reported fatalities on-site. These sites have directed around 239,000 referrals for services such as substance use treatment, medical assessment, mental health care, and housing supports.

That's a good demonstration of politics as medicine on a grand scale. One piece of legislation has saved thousands of lives and helped thousands more receive the health care they deserve.

There is no shortage of skeptics about the value of supervised consumption sites—sometimes from people who promote a treatment- or abstinence-only approach, or sometimes because of accusations of increased crime in their neighbourhoods. To be clear, based on multiple studies, there is no evidence that supervised consumption sites are linked to increased rates of crime.[4] Here's what helps me decide whether or not to support these sites for harm reduction: I try to imagine if it were my son or daughter, my sister or friend who needed a place like that. I might hope that someday they would recover from their dependence on using substances. But first, they would need to stay alive.

During my time as minister of health, I made two key international visits that informed my understanding of international best practices on drug policy—to Switzerland and to Portugal. These two countries offer evidence of the further work we need to do in Canada. Portugal was well known for decriminalizing the possession of small amounts of illicit substances, and I wanted to learn more. I believed this was the direction we should take across the country. I think many people around the cabinet table agreed, but we were not authorized to say this openly.

When Manuel Cardoso visited Canada in the spring of 2017, I took the opportunity to meet him. He's a medical doctor and public health expert, currently with the General Directorate for Intervention on Addictive Behaviours and Dependencies (SICAD) in Portugal. Dr. Cardoso was one of the architects of that country's renowned policy reforms. He was animated and engaging as he described their approach in detail, going back through twenty years of work. It was based on the inalienable human dignity of each person, and that impressed me. Rather than expecting criminal prohibitions (such as incarceration) to manage potential harms associated with substance use,

Portugal has used a lens of social justice and public health. When someone is found in possession of small amounts of drugs for personal use, they are required to appear in front of a regional panel comprised of health professionals, social workers, and drug experts. The person found with drugs may be referred to educational sessions or treatment programs. They may be offered social supports or required to fulfill a community service.[5]

I had an opportunity to visit Portugal to see for myself in late July 2017. It was a joint visit by me and Jody Wilson-Raybould, who was then minister of justice and attorney general. We were both impressed by the efficacy of Portugal's approach to promoting health and reducing the harms of criminalization. The focus of their program was well beyond criminal justice reform. People found in possession of drugs were introduced to a wrap-around set of services that included housing supports, educational opportunities, and access to counselling and treatment options. It's safe to say we came back from that trip more convinced than ever of the merits of this whole-person version of decriminalization. I wish I could have kept pushing this work forward, but a month after returning from Portugal, I was shuffled from the health portfolio to a new area of ministerial responsibility.

The Swiss approach is equally impressive, though their focus has been somewhat different. What both countries have demonstrated is that the harms associated with drugs are managed most effectively by public health programs rather than by policing and criminal prosecution.

In May 2017, I was in Switzerland for the World Health Assembly and I decided to add on a visit with public health officials to learn about their approach to drug policy. The officials who met with me were clearly proud of their work, telling me about their belief that public order was achieved through public health. One of the Swiss police officers said: "My best tool for law and order is supervised consumption sites."

I was eager to tour one of more than twenty clinics where they offer HAT, heroin-assisted therapy. This concept is one of the most effective interventions to promote health, reduce crime, and save lives. It makes so much sense and is now being used in seven European countries.[6] When people are known to be dependent on the use of injection opioids, they will use the drugs that are most available and do what's necessary to acquire those drugs. These are the simple facts behind drug-related crime, not to mention how people who use drugs become susceptible to abuse and trauma in their efforts to access drugs.

The Swiss model demonstrates that when clean heroin is offered as therapy in a respectful and supervised setting, the result goes beyond a sharp drop in drug-related mortality; there is also a range of other positive side effects. These include public benefits such as a massive decrease in property crime, as well as personal benefits for those who receive the therapy and can get their lives back in order—in some cases through continued access to harm-reduction options, and in some cases by achieving abstinence.

This concept made intrinsic sense to me, and I knew the approach was backed by a large body of scientific evidence. At that time in Canada, while there was growing availability of opioid substitution therapies such as methadone and buprenorphine, there was only one clinic that offered clean heroin under the supervision of health workers. It was the Crosstown Clinic in Vancouver's Downtown Eastside.

The key political advisors in the PMO were aware of the benefits of decriminalization. But they were influenced by evidence from polling that this was not widely supported by public opinion. It frustrated me that our policy decisions were driven so much by polling. Of course, democracy demands that politicians listen to the will of the people. But I was convinced that public opinion would come around if the concept was presented to them in a mature and thoughtful manner.

Some might say I was obsessed with making progress on the opioid file. I felt the pressure of human lives at stake, informed by the personal stories I heard, especially from mothers whose children had died from overdoses.

The officials in Health Canada also felt a sense of urgency, and I pushed them to do as much as possible, as quickly as possible. Without question, there were times when I was frustrated that we weren't moving faster. I did not believe the federal government had mounted a sufficient, proportionate response. On Sunday mornings, I would often send an email to Simon Kennedy, my deputy minister, to let him know what was on my mind. On April 23, 2017, my email was particularly directive, and I proposed the following:

1. We need a whole-of-government response. We should prepare a Memorandum for the Cabinet Committee on Intelligence and Emergency Management asking them to evaluate the use of the

Emergencies Act to intervene in the public health
emergency, given recent spikes in overdoses
and deaths.

2. We should appoint a Federal Emergency Task
   Force on Overdose Deaths. This would require a
   clear mandate from the PMO and the Privy Council
   Office. It must be resourced accordingly. It should
   liaise with the Special Advisory Committee on the
   Epidemic of Opioid Overdoses already established by
   Health Canada—and with other appropriate federal
   departments and agencies. It should report directly to
   the Minister of Health, in-person, no less than weekly.

3. It's time to demand data. We must compel the
   provinces to report monthly data including the
   number of overdoses and the number of overdose
   deaths, with information on the drugs associated
   with the deaths. For provinces and major cities,
   we need population estimates of the number of
   people who use drugs.

4. Regarding research, we should begin work
   immediately on a multi-centre trial of alternate
   approaches to managing addiction and drug
   possession. This should include a comparison
   of results of different models of Opioid Agonist
   Therapy as well as the Swiss model. We should
   work with law enforcement to test the Portuguese

model in which violators appear before a health/
justice panel and are offered rehabilitation,
treatment, social support, and trauma therapy.

5. At FNIHB (the First Nations and Inuit Health Branch),
    we need to support universal best-practices for
    the management of problematic substance use.
    We will require the same monthly data reporting
    as provinces and territories. The full range of pre-
    vention, treatment, and harm reduction services
    should be available on reserve. All cases of overdose
    must be offered social support, mental health crisis
    intervention, trauma therapy, and access to detoxi-
    fication or Opioid Agonist Therapy.

6. Regarding Supervised Consumption Sites, we need
    an urgent approval of the BC applications. We need
    a procedure for expedited approval in areas of high
    need. There should be an incentive to link these to
    comprehensive support services and treatment.

7. As for the federally funded pan-Canadian health
    organizations, I would like to request an urgent
    in-person report on how the Mental Health Com-
    mission of Canada and the Canadian Centre for
    Substance Use and Addiction are supporting the
    government's efforts to address the overdose crisis.
    They should also be linked to the emergency
    task force.

—

To his credit, the deputy minister always took these messages seriously. I know he was balancing other forces and hearing other voices that may not have been aligned with my pleas to do more. He took very earnestly his obligations to be a non-partisan public servant, but I believe he was an ally in the efforts on harm reduction.

With the help of the bureaucracy and my minister's office, we did manage to get one piece of important regulatory work done despite the angst of the PMO. We overturned a ban previously associated with evidence-based physician-supervised heroin-assisted treatment to make it available via the Special Access Program. Then we fast-tracked a proposal to allow for the bulk import and use of medications that have been authorized in certain other countries but are not yet authorized in Canada to address urgent public health needs. This included the ability to import diacetylmorphine, a.k.a. heroin, in bulk for use at facilities such as the Crosstown Clinic, where I first learned that we needed to make these regulatory changes. I am certain that this improved the quality of life for people who were served there.

Our team got a lot done in the twenty-two months that I was minister of health. I believe this was because we felt such a sense of resolve around the files where our work could mean life or death for those affected by our decisions (or lack thereof). When I look back now, I'm thankful that we kept such a pace, and I wonder if we could have moved even faster. It felt like my time in each ministerial portfolio was an opportunity to pick up the baton of a relay from those who had come before me. My job was to run with it, knowing I was up against a clock. I also knew that I should always be ready to pass the baton, with the hope that I had positioned the next runner to be successful.

The hardest part about being moved out of the health portfolio in August 2017 was not being able to continue that focus on drug policy. I received so many positive messages from people I had worked with, especially the mothers whose children had died from overdoses.

I saw the loveliest message of all on Twitter a couple of weeks after I was shuffled out of the health portfolio. It was from journalist and author Travis Lupick. He wrote: "It's crazy how ppl on the streets of the #DTES talk abt @janephilpott's transfer. 'Cant believe she's gone.' Like she died & they lost a friend."[7]

I hope the people in Vancouver's Downtown Eastside still consider me their friend. I will be forever grateful for the way they welcomed and accepted me into their community. In 2022, I was invited to be a member of the Global Commission on Drug Policy—a reminder that we can be moved off our path, and that some tools are taken out of our hands, but there are always new devices to pick up, to continue the work.

Getting a seat at the cabinet table was one of the greatest gifts I have ever received. It was not the designation or the status that thrilled me. It was the fact that I had direct access to the machinery of government, and that could be leveraged to mend things that were broken in the legal and policy framework of our nation. It is no exaggeration to say that, as minister of health, I could make decisions that would save hundreds, maybe thousands of lives. The institutions of government in Canada are solidly and functionally designed, so that when people and circumstances are aligned, that machinery can be used to make us a healthier nation and a more just society.

All that to say: politics is a force for good. Sadly, it is abused and misused to the point that its potential for public benefit becomes contaminated. The premise of democracy is to choose people who will represent us and, in that capacity, establish and sustain the rules of the land. We expect them to do so in a way that will benefit everyone, that will allow for a peaceful, healthy, and productive society.

CHAPTER 13

Using Clinical Skills in Politics

My time in politics came to an end as part of a larger political story. To recount my version of the whole saga would be outside the scope of this book, but it was related to attempts in 2018 by the PMO, some ministers, and some political staff to pressure then attorney general Jody Wilson-Raybould to intervene in the prosecution of a criminal trial involving the SNC-Lavalin engineering company. Given there should be no political interference with any criminal prosecution, she would not agree to do so and was subsequently moved to another portfolio. I did not support what the government did, or how they handled it. I did not want my presence in cabinet, or my silence, to imply my consent for actions that I deemed to be wrong. I had no other option but to resign from cabinet.

I had hoped to stay on as a Liberal MP. In my view, a minister must be in solidarity with the prime minister, but there should be room for a non-cabinet MP to disagree with the government's approach, even if they are from the same party. The PM saw things differently. On April 2, 2019, he removed me from the Liberal caucus. I became an independent MP.

One week after I was ejected from my party, my clinical skills were summoned in response to an MP who had collapsed in her seat. It happened during Question Period, as then parliamentary secretary Omar Alghabra was responding to a question about international trade. When the Speaker of the House interrupted him to alert everyone to the medical emergency, I immediately jumped up from my seat. It's a reflexive reaction trained into all doctors. When someone's life might be in danger, we run to help. Because I was no longer with the governing party, I was sitting high up in the corner of the chamber. An amusing video on YouTube shows me scooting across the aisle, trying to move quickly and gracefully in my high-heeled shoes, but taking the long way around out of respect for the rules of decorum in the House of Commons.

One of those rules is that MPs must not get between the Speaker and the mace. The large ceremonial mace, made of gold-plated sterling silver, is the symbol of the Speaker's authority, and it sits on a big table in front of the Speaker's chair. It would have been faster to get to the person in need if I'd taken the shortcut between the Speaker and the mace, but once again, I acted with the force of habit—this time from my MP training. I ran around the table and then back a couple of aisles to get to the seat of the Liberal colleague who had fainted. I should note I did fail my parliamentary training on one count. When MPs move across the floor, they are supposed to bow to the Speaker. I decided that rule was dispensable under the circumstances. I'm happy to report that the MP who collapsed made a fast and full recovery.

—

I've already said the goals of medicine and politics are highly aligned—that is, to improve people's lives. The methodologies used are different, but some of the vocational skills needed to reach those shared objectives are similar. Elected officials bring a range of expertise to their roles. They do not have a uniform skillset—nor should they—though there are some basic competencies that facilitate effective political service. In a democracy, we elect people and give them the profound responsibility of setting the rules that govern our society, including its communities. The test to prove one's fitness for public office is a political one—the ability to win an election. Opportunities to advance in politics are politically determined too. Simply put, democracy does not necessarily mean skills-based governance. A massive pool of talent may be relegated to the back benches. Worse still, some of the smartest, most gifted Canadians would never consider a career in politics, though we could use their wisdom to find our way in these turbulent times. Would that power and proficiency were better aligned.

By contrast, regulated health professionals cannot practise their vocation without validating that they have the required knowledge, skills, and attitudes. Medical education in Canada is almost entirely competency-based. That is, you may not advance in your training or graduate based on the number of courses you've taken or the number of hours in the lab and classroom, but according to a demonstration that you are capable in the relevant domains.

I respect the fact that in all democracies, not just ours, elections are the way to validate someone's fitness for public office. That said, many current political problems—and the distrust and even rage that people have toward governments—are linked to the shortcomings of some of those in power: greed, narcissism, putting politics ahead of people, and poor communications, especially on issues like health. Earning back the confidence that should exist between Canadians and a democratic system that is the envy of other countries starts with the representatives we elect and how good they are, not just at getting elected and staying in power but at implementing real change that serves Canadians for the better. *Health for All* is the title of this book, of course, and it's a term I have repeated often throughout its pages. Achieving this goal is possible, but we need political leaders with the knowledge, skills, and attitudes to make it a reality.

Could politicians benefit from professional development in areas deemed to be core competencies? Groups such as the Samara Centre for Democracy, a Canadian non-partisan resource for research on democracy, would say yes. They have repeatedly noted the shortage of basic training for Members of Parliament.[1] Implementing such training would require some consensus about what those crucial capabilities should be. A set of essential competencies has been articulated for unelected public servants,[2] but not so much for elected representatives.

For the purposes of this book, given the shared themes of medicine and politics, I thought it would be valuable to consider some of the clinical skills that health professionals are expected to achieve—and which of those would be helpful in politics. The science of how to train health workers has been in a state of continuous quality improvement for well over a century. If we can always do better at educating doctors and nurses, maybe we could apply some of these findings to the development of politicians, which could benefit political culture and increase the effectiveness of those who run our governments and write the laws.

Doctors are trained to have a long list of clinical talents. Many of these abilities are learned by other health professionals too. The physical exam proficiencies, such as taking a blood pressure measurement or using a stethoscope to listen to the heart and lungs, would obviously not be very helpful in politics. But other competencies related to decision-making and communication are highly transferable.

No doubt many other vocations would have a set of skills that might be helpful for politicians too. But what the public expects from doctors and politicians is similar: we want them to listen; to understand our needs; to protect us from future harms; and to find cures for what ails us. Given the alignment of the two vocations, it's worth exploring which skills from health care might be transferable to public office. Here are some options.

SOAP Notes

I'd like to start by celebrating the miraculous power of something called SOAP notes. Perhaps a similar instrument of reason, as simple and sturdy as this, exists in many other fields of work, but I can tell you that health care runs on the force of this exquisite little organizing tool.

Almost every health care clinician in North America could describe SOAP notes to you. They seem to me like a natural wonder that has been with us forever. But in fact, it's been only half a century. Their invention is attributed to the late Dr. Lawrence Weed, a professor of medicine at Yale University, who is also known as the father of the problem-oriented medical record.[3] The literature says that Dr. Weed first described the use of SOAP notes around 1972.

SOAP notes are an orderly way of documenting inside a medical record. SOAP stands for: Subjective, Objective, Assessment, and Plan. The Subjective is the patient history. What is the story? What symptoms does the patient describe? Every clinical-skills instructor will tell you that the patient's history (when available) is the most important part. Listening well to the patient's own narrative, in response to good questions, always provides the best clues to the diagnosis.

The Objective part is the findings from examinations or tests. This is about obtaining data. What are the vital signs? What did you learn from the physical examination? What are the lab tests and other objective results?

Then comes the Assessment. What are the possible explanations? Here's where a good set of clinical competencies shows its power. Doctors are trained to commit to a diagnosis. Ideally, you can think of a few plausible explanations. This is called the differential diagnosis, and you're taught to write down a list of all the possibilities—not just a list of symptoms and signs, but the possible root causes. That is, you're not supposed to write down "abdominal pain"—that's a symptom, not a diagnosis. You're supposed to document the most likely causes of that pain. Even if you are not entirely sure, and need to get more information, you are trained to write down your assessment, ideally a working diagnosis.

Finally, the Plan. You need to commit to one and write it down. What other tests need to be done? What treatments will you suggest? When will you check in again to reassess?

Clinicians start to organize their work in the form of SOAP notes. They go through this process so many times a day that it becomes automatic. I used this approach when I was in politics, and it was reflexive. These are completely transferable skills, and it turns out that politicians might benefit from the approach.

You start with listening (Subjective). You need to listen to a lot of people, and hear their concerns and perspectives, to understand their lived realities. Then you look for the facts (Objective). What can you learn from the data? What are the measures of the problem? Is the problem getting better or worse? What is the pulse?

It is the Assessment part that seems to be challenging for politicians, because they aren't generally in the habit of telling people, by committing out loud, let alone in writing, their analysis of a situation. Yet, the public longs for this from our political leaders. In response to some media clips, we're tempted to shout: *Please don't just describe the symptoms. We can all see that.* We often feel that politicians are insulting our intelligence when they state *only* the obvious. We want to hear their best analysis of the problem at hand, and the possible explanations they are considering.

Most important of all, we want to know if they have a Plan. What are the next steps? And if they don't have an answer, how are they going to find out more? When should we check back?

Let's run through a brief example to show how SOAP notes could work in politics. I'll use the problem of the shortage of affordable housing, recalling that shelter is one of the most essential determinants of health.

S: A twenty-three-year-old woman wants to move away from home for college. She can't find a place to rent for less than $2,000 a month. Even if she could work full-time (which she can't if she's going to attend classes), her rent could use up more than three-quarters of her income. Her options are: to get a room only; to get a roommate; to add to her debt-load; or to give up on her dream of moving away from her parents' home to go to college.

O: This young woman is like so many of her peers who struggle to afford a place to live. Rental costs have skyrocketed. Across Canada, as of September 2023, the average cost of renting a one-bedroom apartment was $1,844 a month—an 18.3 percent increase over the previous year.[4]

Additional objective data could include information about the pace of construction of new homes, population projections, and regional policies that impact housing supply and rental rates.

A: The political analysis has to go beyond empathy. On the surface, the problem is that rental prices have pushed the cost of living in Canada to the point that young adults are frustrated and fearful about their future.[5] The differential diagnosis of root causes could include:

> **Housing supply:** The Canada Mortgage and Housing Corporation made a projection in 2022 (and re-affirmed it in 2023) that Canada needs an additional 3.5 million housing units by 2030 to restore affordability—that means adding half a million more housing units per year, above the business-as-usual pace of new building.[6]

Rapid population growth: There is an influx of temporary residents related to demands on the post-secondary sector to bring in revenues from international students.

High interest rates and inflation: These forces push the population toward long-term renting instead of buying, thereby putting pressure on rental rates.

P: The young woman may be eligible for some very modest rental assistance. Otherwise, she's left with the options she outlined. The real political plan is a longer-term one: to get on with manufacturing the homes that Canada needs. This requires all orders of government working to amend any hindering regulations and spur the construction of more rental units.

In the SOAP notes approach, the government in question would present a meticulous plan for accelerating construction of new homes. It could be by way of tax incentives, direct investments, and accelerating innovation. The plan must be more than rhetoric. It must have targets, timelines, and a commitment for regular public updates.

Managing Uncertainty

The second great skill that clinicians have to acquire is the ability to manage uncertainty. When doctors express their uncertainty—to their peers and their patients—I don't see weakness. What I see is humility, their willingness to admit that they don't know everything. That's how you learn.

Medicine is not only a science, based on reason. It is also an art. Sometimes the diagnosis and treatment are obvious, but they are rarely without at least a bit of ambiguity. Every person is different. The way they respond to a pathogen can be unique. The way they respond to a treatment can be quite different. Often, the lack of certitude is minor, but at times the uncertainty is expansive and anxiety-provoking. The clinician has the task of acknowledging any lingering doubt and reassuring the patient there is a wise path forward, even if it is not entirely clear or predictable. Doctors manage the uncertainty by choosing wisely about further investigations. We manage insecurity by scheduling a follow-up visit, sometimes in a few minutes, other times in a few weeks. Sometimes managing uncertainty is an exercise in watchful waiting, based on an expectation that medical conditions usually reveal more clues over time.

Life is uncertain. The public does not expect political leaders to have all the answers. We know they don't know everything, and we are willing to hear that. We would like them to be honest, to tell us when they are not sure, but also to indicate that they have a good plan to manage the uncertainty. The public plea is this: *Please tell us what the working hypothesis is and what tests you're going to do to find out more. Please tell us you have analyzed the options and the risks associated with each possible path, that you have decided about next steps, and that you are going to reassess at the right time interval, to adjust the plan accordingly.*

This is the kind of leadership we longed for during the COVID-19 pandemic. We didn't expect leaders to be able to predict the future, but we wanted them to be honest with us about options. Imagine if political leaders spoke to us like a skilled clinician in the face of medical uncertainty, but with the reassurance that we would always hear the truth.

This might have been particularly helpful early in the pandemic, when there was tremendous uncertainty. On the question of border closures, for example, the federal government was no doubt weighing conflicting opinions in the guidance it received from experts in public health and international health regulations. Even hearing an admission that there was contradictory advice might have been helpful—in the same way a doctor might share with a patient that there is a lack of consensus on how to treat prostate cancer, for example.[7] Yet, in either the political or the clinical case, after sharing the conflicting evidence they were weighing, they could offer a preliminary plan, a timeline for when it would be reviewed, and a frank confession that they might change direction if new information became available.

Managing Mistakes

Doctors and other health professionals make mistakes. Sometimes the mistakes are small, almost inconsequential. But some medical errors cause disasters, even death. I am thankful to be part of a profession that teaches its practitioners how to deal with mistakes, large and small. This is a feature of the curriculum from the very start. Physicians and other health care professionals are trusted, in part, because we are taught to be honest above all. We are trained not to hide behind errors. We are instructed about how to break bad news. We practise how to admit errors and how to apologize. This is done through role play and simulated practice sessions. We are educated in how to learn from our mistakes and, ideally, never make the same mistake again.

Here's what doctors are trained to do about medical mistakes:

1. Take responsibility and admit the mistake;
2. Tell the person(s) who may have been harmed and apologize to them;
3. Fix the mistake if possible, and if not, reduce any potential harm;
4. Examine what went wrong and why; and
5. Implement systemic procedural changes to minimize the likelihood that similar mistakes will ever happen again.

Every doctor could tell you about the errors that haunt them. I think of a few cases where I made a diagnosis too late. In all likelihood, an earlier diagnosis might not have appreciably changed the final outcome, but I will never forget those cases, and I would never miss the diagnosis if a similar case appeared again. One mistake was early in my family medicine career, when I gave a one-year-old child the vaccination that should have been given at eighteen months of age. It shook me and I felt sick about it. I remember how nervous I was to tell the parents about the error. I also know that I never made an immunization schedule error again because of a system I developed to check myself.

Admitting mistakes is never easy. At the same time, it is so powerful. In my experience, patients are remarkably understanding and forgiving. They don't expect health professionals to be perfect. But they do expect and respect honesty. They deserve it too. They want to know that people and systems will learn to do better. Can you imagine how we could transform politics if we had a culture of admitting mistakes and learning from them?

In 2019, in a story that made headlines for months—and to which I alluded at the beginning of this chapter—I believed the government had made a serious mistake in pressuring the attorney general to interfere with the prosecution of a criminal trial. From my perspective, this was a grave error, one that put the foundations of democracy itself at risk. Sadly, it led to the resignation of Jody Wilson-Raybould from cabinet and thereby the loss of Canada's first Indigenous minister of justice and attorney general. In the weeks that followed, during two separate conversations, my advice to the prime minister was to admit that his government had made a mistake. I explained what I had learned about how to manage medical errors and the steps above. I thought an authentic expression of regret could have been a healing act, one that would build trust and transparency, and alter political culture for the better. He chose not to take that advice. I chose to resign from cabinet because I could not support the government's actions on this file.

I'd like to see democratic representatives trained to admit mistakes, the way health professionals are. The training would not be hard, but the culture change could be seismic. Honesty about your own errors, combined with humility, would be refreshing in politics. Honesty is disarming. It is respectful. Its opposite is an affront to people's intelligence.

Persuasion

Health professionals are exceptionally gifted at the art of gentle persuasion. Family doctors are especially well set up to be effective at this because we have had time to develop respectful, long-term relationships. That allows us to gradually gain the trust that is necessary to settle the minds of those who are fearful or skeptical about science, and to do so in a way that leaves the patient's dignity intact. This skill has been put to the test in recent years, but it is worth pausing here to find some lessons from how we've managed this over our years in practice.

There are many examples from primary care of when the art of persuasion is required—helping patients with advice about whether to take, or not to take, antibiotics; reviewing the risks and benefits of various treatments for high cholesterol; or deciding how to manage the results of an elevated prostate-specific antigen test. These discussions are core business for family doctors.

It is true that there is usually a differential in both power and scientific knowledge between a doctor and a patient. Even so, most family doctors and other health professionals have learned the art of persuasion in such a way that it does not come across as meritocratic hubris. That is, in most subsets of our culture, it doesn't work to say, condescendingly, "I'm a doctor. I'm a scientist. Trust me and don't ask questions." That may have worked in generations gone by. It doesn't work in Canada now. It's demeaning and ineffective.

A contemporary example of when the superpower of empathetic persuasion is needed is in the face of vaccine hesitancy. Since long before the COVID-19 pandemic, pediatricians, family doctors, nurses, and public health officials have dealt with people, particularly parents of young children, who are anxious about the risks of vaccination. Here's what we learned: The hesitancy of parents trying to decide about childhood vaccinations comes from a good place, a place of wanting to do no harm to a child. It's a big decision, and if you've heard frightening stories, even inaccurate stories, it's natural to wonder whom to trust. It is never helpful to shame those parents, to imply they are stupid or malevolent, or to ridicule them. I always tried to find common ground, to affirm their desire to make wise decisions for their children. I tried to inform them in a way they could understand.

Citing scientific literature is not always an effective way to win a debate. One approach I used with patients who were hesitant about vaccines was to share what I had seen in Niger. Without trying to be frightening, I told them about children who had developed blindness as a consequence of measles. On rare occasions, I told them about our daughter, who died because there was not an effective vaccination for meningococcus when she was a child. I explained why I made sure that my own children were fully vaccinated, and then I listened again to their concerns. It was a dialogue. I sought to understand their anxiety. To my relief, in almost every case, even if it took months of conversations, my patients would eventually decide to go ahead with childhood vaccinations.

It is regrettable in the context of COVID-19 that some politicians see science as a wedge rather than something to draw us together—using the issue of vaccines to get votes, and not a way to protect health.[8] There were numerous disappointing examples of *how not to* persuade people to follow public health advice. During the 2021 Canadian election campaign, the incumbent PM spoke about "anti-vaxxer mobs" and their "racist, misogynistic attacks."[9] I doubt that villainizing people who question the science about vaccines convinced many of them to find the courage to overcome their anxiety. Sadly, people who weren't successfully persuaded to be vaccinated were disproportionately among those who later died of COVID-19.[10] I wish leaders had looked to primary care clinicians more often for advice about how to win the hearts and minds of skeptics.

To that end, in these times of social division and polarization, health professionals are proceeding with caution. We know that public confidence in science, and therefore in medicine, is not what it used to be. We do not take the historic trust of the public for granted. Trust must be earned. Outside of a life-threatening emergency, it must not be assumed. It is the payback that results from forbearance with, and respect for, people whose lives and learnings are often different from the health worker—and not to be dismissed. That's why we keep listening, offering insights from the art and science of medicine, and gently urging where necessary. This is a skill worth sharing. Trust is worth gaining. It is a currency that can save lives.

Professionalism

Health care trainees don't simply have to complete a set of courses; they have to demonstrate the achievement of certain attributes before they can be formally qualified and credentialed. One of the competencies expected of physicians is professionalism. This particular competency is the hardest one to define, the most difficult one to teach, and arguably the most important one to achieve if one hopes to have a successful and effective medical career.

Medical educators argue about how to define professionalism. As such, there is no single, agreed-upon definition. You know it when you see it—and you definitely know it when you don't see it—but it's hard to pin down. A systematic review of definitions[11] offers common themes, suggesting that medical professionalism is a set of values and behaviours including:

- trustworthiness, honesty, integrity, compassion, altruism, empathy, and respect for others;
- subordination of self-interest;
- high ethical and moral standards;
- accountability to a social contract;
- commitment to excellence and lifelong learning; and
- the ability to self-reflect, self-regulate, and incorporate feedback.

In my role as dean of Queen's Health Sciences and director of the School of Medicine, my team and I are accountable to ensure that graduates of our programs demonstrate professionalism before they go into practice. When physicians fail to exhibit professionalism in practice, it leads to legitimate complaints, fulsome investigations, and grim consequences. Doctors mess up on this from time to time. That's why the health sector won't stop upholding professionalism as a serious societal expectation.

Have a look at that list of values and behaviours again. This is not the list of attributes commonly ascribed to politicians. From what I've seen, many people go into politics with those values and the aspiration to display a set of behaviours to match, but there is enormous pressure to act quite differently after arriving in public office. I felt that pressure when I arrived in Ottawa. I brought decades of practice in medical profession-alism with me, and then found that I was encouraged to behave in an entirely different manner. Let me offer a few examples.

Having a seat at the cabinet table was a profound respon-sibility. I felt that weight. I worked hard to be prepared for discussions at cabinet committee meetings or the weekly full cabinet meeting. I took seriously my duty to weigh in when I had something worthwhile to contribute or recognized an angle that had not been considered. I tried not to succumb to groupthink. When my views differed from others', I added comments respectfully, and they were accepted in the same spirit. I particularly liked Treasury Board meetings because we had such intelligent briefings from the secretariat. I felt the burden of my obligation to examine plans for federal spending, so I asked a lot of questions. The Treasury Board secretariat appreciated the questions, recognizing their own accountability. They spent hours preparing for those meetings. Behind closed doors, the behaviours of professionalism were evident and appreciated.

It was when we left the relative security of the cabinet room and moved out to the legislature, the House of Commons, that different behaviour was asked for and rewarded. I found this unsettling, to say the least. Many colleagues entered that arena as if it were a game, a theatre, or a reality-TV show. This was especially true when it came to the daily Question Period, when MPs of all parties would prepare questions for the gov-ernment—that is, the cabinet ministers, including the prime minister. Before Question Period, the cabinet ministers were expected to show up for a practice grilling of questions from political staff, as if we were in a locker room preparing for game time. Every minister was provided with a massive binder with pre-written answers for the questions most likely to be asked. The binders were organized by topic, with the idea that you could find the answer quickly once you heard the theme of the question.

I understood the need to be prepared, but I hated the contrived nature of it all. I hated that the apparent goal of Question Period was to score political points, if possible, and if not, at least to get out unscathed. I do not remember hearing the coaching staff refer to the fact that this was our opportunity to be accountable to Canadians.

I was unimpressed by the habit of ministers reading pre-written answers in Question Period. I did occasionally use the papers given to me, especially for answers in French, in which I felt less confident about speaking without a script. Otherwise, when I received questions from the opposition, I seldom used the answers from my binder. I tried to speak frankly about what I knew. I tried to answer the question. I'd like to see a Question Period in which ministers do not carry binders full of answers. If you can't answer questions related to your portfolio with honesty, candour, and intelligence, I wonder if you should be a cabinet minister.

I relished the test of doing well in the Question Period. You have only thirty-five seconds to provide an answer, and I challenged myself to think fast on my feet. I tried to give actual information in plain language, and Liberal colleagues often told me they appreciated the way I answered. One day over lunch in the parliamentary restaurant, when asked for advice on this, I shared with a few MPs the personal formula I had developed for my answers. I figured that in thirty-five seconds you had time for about three sentences. I decided you could organize those sentences with standard themes. My formula was this: Grace, Wisdom, Courage. The first sentence was to be gracious, thanking the member opposite for a smart question or acknowledging their work on the file to be discussed. The wisdom sentence was an opportunity to share a fact, something that I knew to be true about the issue in question. The courage sentence was a chance to say what we were going to do, what action we were going to take. Many days, I sat there hoping to get questions, mostly so I could tell the country about the important work we were doing, but I also loved the challenge of trying to think quickly and provide an intelligent answer.

It bugged me that what our political staff were guided to care about was not how intelligent the answers were but how we could use the opportunity to score points. They loved it when we gave arrogant answers like: "I'll take no lessons on Issue X from the party opposite, who spent ten years destroying the country, blah, blah, blah."

I hated that so much. What an awful answer. What did it mean that the government wouldn't take lessons from other elected representatives? Even if the lesson was that another party's approach hadn't worked, that was still a lesson. I refused to use that line.

One memorable day, two of the young women on my political staff team nervously approached me to say the PMO had instructed them to tell me I needed to be more aggressive and political in my answers. They wanted me to say more things that would tear down the opposition. My staffers knew that was not my style, but they were the messengers, so I tried not to shoot them. I simply said: "If that senior person in the PMO has a message of this nature, they should not use you as a channel. If they don't like my courteous answers, they can tell me directly. But I will not spout nastiness and I will not change who I am. That person in the PMO is not the cabinet minister. I am." Those two staff members never tried to manipulate the tone of my answers again. They knew I was right. I'm sorry the PMO tried to use them in such a ruthless manner.

The tone of discourse in the House of Commons continues to deteriorate. I get the sense most people have given up on the hope that decorum will ever be restored. I'm not so pessimistic. We simply haven't seen a concerted effort, directed from the leadership of any party, for MPs to behave with professionalism at all times. It should not be too much to ask of MPs that they speak and behave inside and outside of the House of Commons with restraint and dignity.

There is a Code of Conduct document for Canadian Members of Parliament.[12] Its contents include matters of attendance, prevention of harassment, and the prevention and resolution of conflicts of interest. There are also Standing Orders that offer high-level guidance about the speech and behaviour of members. Those are the bare minimum of what the public should expect from its representatives. Perhaps parties or their leaders could introduce an added obligation for members to demonstrate professionalism, with the training and assessment protocols to make it work.

Collaboration

Nothing could happen in health care without collaboration. Health care is a complex sector. It involves teams of people with a range of roles. In Part One, I described a long list of the types of health workers needed to comprise a highly effective primary care team. The same would be true of care delivery in a hospital context. You take people with different but complementary training and put them on a team. If everyone performs to the top of their scope and tasks are shifted according to the needs of each patient, you have the best outcomes.

Most health professionals will admit that working with people from other disciplines can be challenging. We need continuous improvement in the competency of collaboration, but we know that we can't get much done without it. There are long-standing hierarchies in medicine, and we struggle to ensure that everyone is appropriately valued and respected for what they bring to the team. But at least you can say that one part of the team doesn't deliberately try to sabotage other members. We have the same goal. We depend on one another. The doctors want and need the nurses to be successful, and vice versa.

One of the big adjustments for me when I arrived in Ottawa as an MP was that it was the first time in my life that my co-workers (in this case, opposition MPs) were explicitly encouraged and expected to sabotage the success of my efforts. It's the darnedest, most counterproductive thing about partisan politics. We elect people to go to Ottawa to represent the best interests of their community and their country. In theory, there are 338 people in the House of Commons, each of whom wants the best for the country. But instead of collaborating with one another and using their time for effective governance, they spend vast amounts of time and effort trying to make their colleagues fail.

I'll offer one example of wasted time: Of all the topics I was asked about during the daily Question Period in the House of

Commons, the most-asked category was questions about the Canada Health Transfer—especially in 2016, when we were negotiating a new agreement with provinces and territories. We had decided that the CHT should no longer grow at a rate of 6 percent a year, especially because the annual increase in spending on health by the provinces was growing at less than 2 percent. We were going to change the guaranteed rate of annual growth to 3 percent a year—but it would still grow substantially every year. Opposition members from other parties insisted on characterizing this as a *cut* to the CHT, which it was not.[13] It drove me mad that there were dozens of questions, day after day, that included various versions of that mischaracterization. I understand that Question Period is when all MPs have an opportunity to hold the government to account, but on this topic, the time was used for tedious political theatrics and not for legitimate critique or asking about better ways to improve health care for Canadians.

What an enormous waste of talent and resources. Does it really have to be that way? I dream of witnessing a Canadian Parliament that functions like a health care team. Individuals arrive with different skills, and they are encouraged to work with others to the full scope of those talents—offering constructive criticism and looking for the best ideas from all parties. Tasks are shared and shifted according to who is trained for the job.

I have heard that former prime minister Brian Mulroney was particularly gifted at managing his caucus, and that one of the ways he did so was by inviting parliamentarians to his home for breakfast and then giving them a ride back to Parliament Hill with him.[14] Apparently, he did this particularly when someone was unhappy with how he was managing the government.

What if a PM were to take that idea a step further? What if the PM routinely invited several MPs or senators to his or her home for breakfast? I don't mean just MPs from the same party as the prime minister, either. You could invite a random, cross-partisan group each week to share a meal and get to know one another. Then, over the meal, you could learn about each MP—their personal story, the riding they represent, and what issues matter to them.

It was a children's television host, the late Fred Rogers, who brought the world's attention to a quotation he'd learned from a Benedictine nun, Sister Mary Lou Kownacki, who said: "There isn't anyone you couldn't love once you've heard their story."[15] Parliamentarians are hardly known for loving one another. How transformative could it be if they were to hear one another's stories, learn to appreciate each other, and then work more collaboratively on behalf of Canadians?

CHAPTER 14

The Parable of the Crumbling Cottage

The grandfather of my husband, Pep, was a man named Arthur Crawley, who was a respected accountant in Ottawa. To the family, he was affectionately known as Kop, and he must have been quite a character, because many stories about his adventures are retold even now. Back in 1938, Kop bought an old farm on the shores of Big Rideau Lake, an hour west of Ottawa. Thinking it would be a perfect summer getaway spot for his large extended family, he arranged for a Swiss friend to build a chalet-style log cabin on the site. The European craftsman created a one-of-a-kind structure with rough pine logs of assorted sizes. I assume when the logs were originally stacked on top of one another, they formed properly aligned vertical walls. Well, by the time I became part of the family in the mid-1980s, the cabin by the lake was as much loved as it had been since the 1940s, but the logs had shifted. In some parts, the log-stacks were angling so much that it seemed, with one push, they would collapse outward. In other parts, it appeared that the logs might suddenly roll inward and the whole building would fall in on itself. The family had concocted various contingencies, such as a wide steel cable across the whole main room, which was intended to keep the upper logs from rolling outward. The whole thing was precarious, but it was beloved and usable, a venue for games, meals, and fireside conversations. It was known to family and friends as Windermere.

By the time Pep and I returned from living in Niger in 1998, Windermere had deteriorated considerably. It had become a winter home for bats, birds, and other creatures. Each spring, we cleaned out the snake skins and mouse nests. We hoped some fresh air and cleaning products would overpower the musty smells. The bravest kids were still willing to sleep there overnight, but it had become quite unpleasant.

Something had to be done. Nostalgia for the good old days translated into futility for the present. We spoke to one builder about potential renovations and he told us the building should be condemned. The property was co-owned by Pep, his five siblings, and Pep's dad. (Pep's mom had been killed in a car accident when he was a teenager.) Everyone was emotionally attached to the place, but we agreed that the status quo was unsustainable. However, most of the siblings were not geographically or financially in a position to invest in the property. Meanwhile, with every passing year, it became messier and more hazardous.

Eventually, Pep and I offered a solution. We developed a plan to subdivide the land and sell a couple of lots. We would refinance our home in Stouffville, giving us the resources to buy out his dad and siblings. As sole owners, we acknowledged that renovating Windermere was not an option. It had to be torn down and rebuilt.

The entire log cabin had to be taken down to its founda-tions, although we saved the impressive limestone fireplace. A talented local builder reconstructed the cabin—not with crooked pine logs this time, but he used almost the exact same floor plan. They strengthened the foundations. We tucked in a second bathroom. The kitchen was modernized. The new windows are bigger and brighter than the old ones. Most of the materials were new, but with the original fireplace still at the heart of the building, the same footprint, and the same layout, it still evokes the spirit of the old cabin. Once again, the memories have a place to come alive. The new Windermere can now serve many more generations as a summer abode.

The analogy is not perfect, but there are parallels between a dangerously dilapidated cottage and the state of health care in Canada. It was built generations ago, and is beloved, but is now at risk of falling in on itself, or falling outward—collapsing one way or another. It's a good metaphor for health systems. It's certainly good enough that in 2023, before I had a chance to get this in print, *Globe and Mail* columnist André Picard sim-ilarly compared the frightful decay of Canadian medicare to the rotting condition of the official home of the prime minister, 24 Sussex Drive.[1]

In the case of Windermere, it should have been maintained and strengthened over the years. Maybe the design wasn't perfect in the first place. Or maybe it didn't get originally con-structed as it was envisioned. How could the original builder have anticipated all the environmental conditions it would face over the generations? Eventually all those questions, and the if-onlys, became moot. It would take more than spit and polish to make the place functional and desirable again. We had to be decisive going forward. We had to invest. The good news is there was a way to reconstruct it and still retain the heart and soul of the place.

This is what health care in Canada needs: not more studies, handwringing, and pontification; not just a few tweaks of patchwork window-dressing. We need decisive action, investments, and a reconstruction, almost from the ground up, in a way that retains the soul—that is, the values and principles—of Canadian medicare.

Decisive action on health requires attention to the many layers of well-being. This includes acknowledgement and support for the spiritual roots of wellness (hope, belonging, meaning, purpose) as described in Part Two. It includes the foundational social structures (housing, employment, food security, social inclusion, etc.) as described in Part Three. Most urgently, decisive action is required to overhaul service delivery as described in Part One, resulting in universal access to primary care at the core of health and social services. We can rebuild the rest of the health care system from that base.

So, who needs to make those decisions and act? There's a good deal that individuals, groups, civil society, public institutions, and private corporations can do to promote and protect the health of others. But when you study the deepest underpinnings of well-being, you realize we cannot be a truly healthy country unless we have good governance. That's where the power lies. The greatest responsibility, authority, and resources rest with the political leaders in the highest offices—of the country, the provinces, and the territories.

Decisive Action

It turns out that the political determinants of health are the deepest roots of a country's well-being. In my career, I've gone from thinking that biomedical sciences were the best way to help people be healthy; to figuring out that the real drivers of health are the social determinants, or even the economic determinants; to finally understanding that those social and economic structures are established and upheld by political power. We will never be a country with health for all unless our political leaders make it a top priority, exhibit the courage to make some tough decisions, and then painstakingly watch over the implementation of a new, coordinated national health system rooted in universal access to primary care.

None of the problems or solutions I've described are new in the world of health policy. The ideas are based on hundreds of reports written over decades. Yet health systems remain stuck. Health workers are exhausted, as a trip to any hospital emergency department, for example, will reveal. They work hard every day to keep people alive and well, but when they try to improve the conditions of care, they struggle to make progress. They are more than aware of what's not working and how the systems could be changed, but they don't control the levers to do so. We can't fix broken health systems unless our political leaders make this a top priority and start listening more to the people on the ground. We must urge them to do so, especially with our votes. Then the people who spend their days on the front lines—along with the patients they serve—will be ready and happy to co-create the design and reconstruction of a health system that works for everyone.

Since the towering vision of Tommy Douglas, supported by two prime ministers—John Diefenbaker and Lester B. Pearson—and others from the 1940s to the 1970s, Canada has not enjoyed ambitious political leadership to fundamentally improve health systems in Canada—with the exception of the gritty determination of Monique Bégin, supported by Prime Minister Pierre Trudeau in the early 1980s. The closest we came was with Prime Minister Paul Martin in 2004, when he took on health care as a top federal priority and offered the "fix for a generation" with substantially increased investment, but without a definitive plan about how to deliver reforms in primary care and home care. Perhaps if he had retained power beyond 2006, a strategy would have emerged. Instead, we've been spending more on health care each year, but using the systemic structures of the twentieth century, which are not fit for dealing with the new challenges of our times.

I was federal minister of health for almost two years, and we delivered on many health-related initiatives during that time. But our government did not attempt any bold restructuring of health care. Health was not a top government priority, as it was for Paul Martin twenty years ago—and it was nowhere near the urgent cause it became for the founders of medicare in the last century.

It's a rare political leader who claims they can fix health care, let alone achieve health for all. But we need that genre of nation-building leadership now.

My Hausa friends in Niger taught me a proverb: "Lafiya ita ce uwar kome," which when translated means *Health is the mother of everything.* Health is not the only thing, but it's the mother of everything. Governments have many issues on their agenda—foreign affairs, the economy, climate change, law and order, the list goes on. Health is the purpose and the platform for all of these. Without health, we are not a great nation. Without it, our standard of living is poor, no matter what else we have. That's why it should be very high on the political agenda of all governments—federal, provincial, territorial, and Indigenous. When you are sick, you have one focus, and that's to get back to health. As a country, we are ailing, and our priority should be to get better.

This sentiment is borne out in public opinion surveys. Regardless of which polling company you follow, health care is consistently in the top four or five priorities on the minds of Canadians.[2] Sometimes it's even at the very top of the list, surpassing both inflation and the economy as the most critical issue.[3] So, why do we so rarely see politicians running on a platform with health care near the top of their agenda?

I have a few theories. It starts because many political operatives don't think they can win an election based on health issues. Therefore, they become distracted by efforts to gain or retain power by way of a different narrative. In some cases, they have blinders on, limiting their vision to their ideological priorities; they aren't listening to the people's priorities.

Most politicians have a limited understanding about how health systems work. As a result, policy-makers can't agree on how to fix those systems. They ought to know that health workers on the front lines are surprisingly aligned about what needs to be done—and they're ready to help. And even when politicians know what to do, sometimes their teams simply lack the executive skills to follow through on their health-related promises.

Then there is the problem of timidity. It seems that many of our leaders lack vision and fail to imagine that Canada could provide better systems for care. They get nervous about jurisdictional barriers, which results in federal politicians who won't find the courage to be leaders on health.

Finally, there is the political angst that it will take too long. They don't want to take on an issue that won't be solved in a four-year term. Suffice it to say that a health system overhaul will not happen as long as these points are left unaddressed. Voters will have to make it very clear that we expect this work to be done. We know it will take time, but we have to get started.

I'm cautiously optimistic that conventional wisdom could be changing now that two provincial premiers have come to power with a platform focused on health care—Progressive Conservative Tim Houston in Nova Scotia in 2021, followed by the New Democratic Party's Wab Kinew in Manitoba in 2023. Perhaps the issue is more important than ever in the minds of voters. Political strategists will be watching closely to see if they can deliver on their promises, and if future voters will reward them for putting health first.

A Core Commitment to Equity

There's another core characteristic of political leaders, without which this transformative work will remain on pause. If we want to improve health outcomes, we need to elect representatives and leaders who are driven by the fundamental value of equity. Making this happen is on all of us. This is within the control of every Canadian who is eligible to vote.

Note that I use the words *equity*, *fairness*, and *justice* almost interchangeably. Feel free to pick the one you prefer. The point is that without leadership that upholds these values, we're not going to have efficient health systems. We need to assign the levers of power to people who will use those levers for the common good, to people who believe that every person deserves access to care—and access to all the other societal structures necessary for health. Many people who seek elected office will say they are committed to justice for all. Their actions eventually show if they are genuine or not. Voters need to discern whose words will translate into action.

An authentic understanding of the inequities of society should be a core attribute of the people we put in power. If a leader does not already recognize society's entrenched patterns of injustice, it's hard to imagine they would use their new-found authority to change those patterns.

An equitable world view is not something that a leader can acquire after they've been elected. It has to be deeply woven into their character before they arrive in office because it's too easy to be swayed away from those values once you've been given the privilege and responsibility to lead. Canadian political leaders have considerable control over enormous resources that can be used to shift the structures of society. For that reason, those same leaders have many other powerful, well-resourced voices in their ears. It can be hard for leaders to prioritize the needs of people who don't have all those advantages—and there may not be much incentive to do so.

Nothing drives me forward more than the realization that the world is far from equitable—and the belief that it could be fairer. I am indebted to countless people who have taught me that. I learned it from my patients. I learned it from my neighbours, particularly when we lived in Niger. I learned it from people I have met on my travels in Canada, especially those I have met in isolated Indigenous communities who lack access to basic human necessities like clean water and a decent house to call home. In Canada, the gulf between the haves and the have-nots does not need to be widening at its current record pace.[4] Other countries (most of them European[5]) have done better at reducing economic inequality and promoting the well-being of everyone.

I don't know if I'll ever end up in politics again. But I do have political dreams. I dream of a culture of politics that is healthier and kinder. I dream of the country's leaders being consumed by the pursuit of a fairer Canada and a fairer world. I dream that Canadians will not surrender to the easy path of divisiveness where people are sorted into us and them. I dream Canada will be led up a harder path, one where we stick together and look out for the interests of one another.

The levers of power are held by a small group of individuals in this country—but it's we, the people, who give them that authority. We have an obligation to elect people with the right motivation—and those leaders have a solemn duty to serve for the good of all, to work diligently toward health for all.

Collaborative Implementation

The stakes are high. Up until now, however imperfect our health systems are, there has been a formal commitment to equity, a legal principle requiring that access to care should be based on need and not on the ability to pay. But with so many people struggling to access care, we are at an inflection point. Either we do something dramatic, and soon, or the founding principles of Canadian medicare will not be able to withstand the pressure to give way. Corporations have stepped into the breach. Not surprisingly, they have willing, paying customers who need medical care. Most provinces have not interfered, so companies have an increasingly wide berth to offer private-pay solutions. Businesses have inserted themselves in such substantial numbers that the trend could be hard to reverse. If it continues, more Canadians will pay to get care, which will leave everyone else with worse access, longer waiting lists, and more staff shortages in our publicly funded system. We won't be any closer to the improved health outcomes we're after—and in the end we'll all pay more.

In the opening chapters, I described a Canadian dream of universal access to primary care. To close, I'll describe some scenes from what might be the prequel to that dream.

Let's imagine that in the next federal election at least one of the parties comes forward with a vision of health for all as their overarching priority. Health care is at the top of the agenda, the issue they are running on, and almost everything else flows from that. As such, the rest of the platform sees the future of Canada through a "health in all policies" lens. It includes all the other structural work that enables well-being—affordable housing, lower food costs, action to combat climate change. Health in all policies must also include the crucial work of reconciliation—that is, the implementation of Indigenous rights so that the Indian Act can finally be abolished.

In this dream, Canadians are fully aligned behind, and advocating for, rebuilding the foundations of health care, with the base constructed on universal access to primary health care. In fact, some provinces have made progress in this direction, but it's not universal in any part of the country.

With more substance than rhetoric, federal political leaders commit to health for all—universal access to primary care by 2035. They admit that everyone living in Canada has the right to publicly funded primary health care, just as every child in the country has a right to publicly funded primary and secondary school. This is not just a commitment to care by doctors or in hospitals, which we've had for decades now. This means team-based care in every community. No one will be left out.

These federal politicians understand that provinces have the difficult role of operationalizing this vision, but they unapologetically exercise leadership on health. We are one country after all. If Canadian lawmakers will not ensure that their people have the basic provisions of life, including health care, they are abdicating one of the most rudimentary roles of government.

This time, unlike the usual blame-laying banter that marks federal-provincial-territorial discourse about health care, Canadians hear leaders talk about collaborating with other governments. The dream plan includes a first ministers' meeting on the topic of health care to take place in the first one hundred days of the new federal government, with First Nations, Inuit, and Métis leaders at the table.

That vision of a robust national health system resonates with Canadians. Let's imagine a political mandate is achieved and the wheels are set in motion. Together, the first ministers and their teams affirm the shared vision: they agree that Canadians require universal access to primary care teams. They commission their officials to co-develop the implementation work-plan.

Recognizing that this will require budgets to be realigned so that more health spending goes to primary care—which will save money in downstream costs—the first ministers agree that new investments from the federal government will be dedicated to this cause. Knowing that taxpayers deserve accountability for how these funds will be used, they have their first formal discussion about the content of a Canada Primary Care Act that will lay down the principles for what Canadians can expect regarding the access and services connected to primary care teams. Collaboration and mutual respect are keys to successful implementation. Jurisdictional squabbles can no longer be tolerated. They put lives at risk while people wait for better access to care.

This is the time to rise above our regional divisions, to set aside our parochial thinking. It's time to be a country where we look out for one another, where we treat others as we'd like to be treated ourselves. The achievement of universal access to primary care would mark the next great era of intergovernmental co-operation for the health of Canadians. It would be the biggest step forward for health care in Canada since 1984. Surely, we can make that dream come true.

Epilogue

I was making the final edits on this manuscript on September 9, 2023, when I took a break, checked social media, and saw that Monique Bégin had died the day before. I felt an unexpectedly intense wave of sorrow—and regret that I hadn't reached out to her in recent years. Canada had lost a legend. It was no longer possible to hear her voice out loud, just when we could use someone like her to get us through a nation-wide health care crisis.

This prompted me to have a second look at the memoir Mme Bégin published in 2019.[1] I reread the story of how she manoeuvred the political landscape to legislate access to care through the Canada Health Act. It is the stuff of heroes. The tension of the time reads like a cinematic drama. Here's how it unfolded.

It was the early 1980s. Health care was in crisis.

Provinces were trying to solve their overall fiscal pressures by charging patients to access care. In 1979, Ontario entertained the concept of a user fee of $9.80 a day for patients who stayed in hospital more than sixty days. New Brunswick passed a bill imposing user fees of $6 for outpatient visits, $10 per admission, and $8.50 a day in hospital. The head of the Ontario Hospital Association proposed a $50 user fee for admission to hospital. Several provinces were adding health premiums to provincial taxes.

Meanwhile, doctors were unhappy—demanding more money, billing patients with surcharges, or threatening to leave the public insurance system. Provinces tried to appease the medical workforce with unprecedented raises for doctors' pay, including a stunning 40 percent fee increase in British Columbia in 1981.

Elsewhere doctors were walking off the job. A strike took place in Ontario in April 1982, which was resolved with a new physicians' contract providing a 34 percent raise. Rotating doctors' strikes in Quebec that spring were settled with an 11 percent increase. Doctors in Prince Edward Island opted out of medicare en masse for six months, demanding the ability to extra-bill their patients. Half of Alberta's doctors were already extra-billing.

Woven into these scenes of chaos on the front lines of care is the story of a spunky and principled politician by the name of Monique Bégin, who had been Canada's minister of health and welfare since 1977. In her book, she endearingly admits that until 1979 she "knew almost nothing about medicare."[2] Given the context, what's more frightening is that she perceived from her department officials the sense that she "did not need to worry about or be briefed on the health-care system."[3]

Thankfully, she was skeptical about that advice. In retrospect, it's hard to imagine that it wasn't obvious to everyone that medicare was in a fragile state. She could see that while

the federal government, the provinces, and the medical organizations across the country were squabbling about finances,
it was patients who were going to be the losers. Even modest
financial barriers would keep some people from accessing
the care they needed at the time when their conditions were
easiest to treat. She also recognized that she did not have the
legislative tools to ban extra-billing, nor to limit the ability of
hospitals and clinics to impose user fees.

There were, in fact, no easy answers to the escalating
problems of provincial fiscal pressures, an agitated physician
workforce, and inadequate legal mechanisms to protect the
principle of access to care based on medical need and not on
the ability to pay. Thankfully, the tenacious Mme Bégin was
on the case. While she quietly worked on the solution, exter-
nal observers criticized her for dithering while medicare was
self-destructing. On the government side, she had her own
battles. Medicare was not high on the agenda. Prime Minister
Pierre Trudeau was busy patriating Canada's constitution—not
to mention managing pension reform, high levels of inflation
and unemployment, soaring interest rates, and a postal strike.
But the clock was ticking on medicare.

It took a small team of colleagues and legal advisors to
help Mme Bégin put together what she needed—a new law
to expand the principles of medicare. Four principles were
already in place: universality, comprehensiveness, portability,
and public administration. The part that was not written into
law was accessibility.

Thus was born the Canada Health Act, which offered clarity that the health care insurance plan of each province must
provide:

1. Access to health services without user fees or extra-billing; and
2. Reasonable compensation to medical practitioners based on negotiations that included appropriate mechanisms for dispute resolution.

Given the stability that this law has offered to health systems in Canada for four decades now, you'd think it might have easily moved through the legislative processes. That was not the case.

Mme Bégin faced obstacles inside and outside government. On the inside, she could barely get the file on the schedule of cabinet priorities. It was bumped from the agenda week after week in 1983. When it finally did get to full cabinet, she was so worried about whether it would be approved that she took the exceptional step of writing personal two-page letters in advance to every one of her cabinet colleagues asking for their support and explaining what was at stake.

On the outside, she faced opposition from all ten provinces and "all of organized medicine."[4] In her book, she describes a scenario that she elaborated on to me in a personal conversation, when she approached Pierre Trudeau in the House of Commons one day about her angst. She crouched down in the aisle beside his desk, telling him about all the opposing forces. His vital question was: "Where is the population in all of that?" She answered, "In favour of the bill." His simple response was "That's a sure win—like the Constitution."

Indeed, it was. The bill passed with unanimous consent on April 9, 1984, one of the most iconic and important laws of the nation. But it must be known that it wouldn't have happened without the stubborn determination of Monique Bégin. Medicare as we know it may not have existed today. We could have followed the path of the country south of our border. They pay the highest per capita costs for health care of any country in the world, while simultaneously being one of the few countries where life expectancies are declining, and health outcome gaps between rich and poor have never been wider.[5]

As I imagine the movie version of that drama from the 1980s, I see the scenes of doctors protesting at hospitals and legislative buildings. I see the undeterred minister of national health and welfare lobbying her own colleagues until they understood what had to be done. I see the patients deciding not to seek care because the cost of food and rent had to be weighed against the out-of-pocket costs to see a doctor. Most of all, I see Monique Bégin as the unlikely protagonist—and I think about how lucky we are that she persevered against the odds.

As a sequel, I consider the movie that might be made about health in Canada in the 2020s. A devastating pandemic swept across the nation—killing more than fifty thousand Canadians. In its wake, the health workforce is diminished and demoralized. Millions of Canadians have no front door into the health care system. The fate of medicare hangs in the balance. Most politicians are too distracted by other priorities to take on this challenge. It's easier to let corporations step into the gap, and to look the other way when people who are willing and able to use their own money to pay for care are moved to the front of the queue. Others anxiously wait to be served by the health workers who refuse to abandon the public system.

It doesn't have to end that way. We can create Medicare 2.0, the twenty-first-century transformation. Leaders like Monique Bégin can emerge to confront the forces of health system disintegration. We can demand a healthier form of politics—one that moves from oratory to action. The steps toward universal access to care are known; those who hold the levers of government can take on the hard work of implementing them. Meanwhile, Canadians can advocate for a health lens in all public policies. Finally, we can revive and sustain a national culture that nurtures the needs of our souls—to have hope, belonging, meaning, and purpose.

Without health, little else matters. Without health for all, everyone suffers.

The powers that drive us toward an ever more inequitable society must be tackled head on. It's up to us—all of us who call Canada home—to step into the breach, to protect the principles of the Canada Health Act, to elect people who will fight for fairness, and to not give up until each one of us can access the care we need.

Canada has everything it takes to be a nation where each person could enjoy their right to the highest attainable standard of health. But becoming a healthier country does not happen by the force of good intentions. We have to pull together, prioritize our collective well-being, and put in the hard work to construct a society that is functional and fair for all. Let us not squander our days. People are waiting.

Acknowledgements

I am indebted to a huge number of people for their help in making this book happen. I'll start with my agent, Suzanne Brandreth, who believed I had a book in me and gently helped me sort out what I needed to say. Thank you to Stephanie Sinclair at McClelland & Stewart for your confidence in this project. A special thanks to my editor, and publisher of Signal, Doug Pepper for your professional guidance and the hours you spent making the manuscript better—and to copy editor Linda Pruessen, whose painstaking attention to detail offered the final improvements.

My dear friends Sarah Barclay, Michael Fekete, Jen Hess, Jen Keenan, Mary Lovatt, Allan Reesor-McDowell, Julie Weiss, and Jody Wilson-Raybould all read parts of the manuscript and were exceedingly generous with their advice and reassurance along the way. So many colleagues at Queen's University were involved in one way or another: Special thanks to David Barber, Erin Brennan, Steve Brooks, Celina Caesar-Chavannes, David Clements, Barbara Crow, Vincent de Paul, Catherine Donnelly, Colleen Flood, Colleen Grady, Roger Pilon, Duncan Sinclair, and Jen Valberg. I had enthusiastic help from medical students Matthew Hynes, Patrick Kim, and Devyani Premkumar.

Over the years, ideas found in this book came from hundreds of colleagues across the country. For expert feedback on the manuscript, I'm indebted to some of Canada's best family doctors, including Rick Glazier, Tara Kiran, Danielle Martin, Ryan Meili, and Meb Rashid. For additional perspectives on health systems, Brian Golden introduced me to Rosemary Hannam, who cheered me on and helped with fact-finding. I'm also thankful to Rachel Doran, Chris Ekeigwe, Carol Hopkins, Craig Kuziemsky, Lorraine Lam, Deb Matthews, Cora Morgan, Christopher Mushquash, and Marcel Saulnier, each of whom answered questions or read sections of the book to assist with the details.

The biggest debt of gratitude is for my family—starting with my mom, Audrey Little, as well as my sisters, Judy Boivin, Karen Congram, and Kathy Hoogsteen. All three sisters provided content advice, informed by their lived experiences in the health sector. My wonderful husband, Pep, offers non-stop support for each endeavour I undertake. In this case, he showed up with food and forbearance; encouragement and editorial advice; plus many insightful ideas to consider. Our children (and their partners), Bethany (and Alex), Jacob (and Emily), David (and Juliana), and Lydia are my kindest critics and my most patient cheerleaders. Bethany gave additional input from her perspective as a family doctor. Finally, our grandchildren—Mikayla and Sulaiman—are too young to read the manuscript, but they give me the motivation I need to keep fighting for a healthier world—for their future.

Notes

Introduction

1   Kiran, Tara. "We need bold reform to fix family health care;
    Access to local support should be guaranteed. One possible
    solution: Expand team-based aid from medical professionals."
    Globe & Mail (Toronto, Canada) (2023): A13–A13.

Chapter 1: A Canadian Health Care Dream

1   "OurCare Data Explorer," OurCare, n.d., https://data.ourcare.ca/
    all-questions. Accessed September 9, 2023.

2   Tina Yazdani, "Estimated 11,000 Ontarians Died Waiting for
    Surgeries, Scans in the Past Year," CityNews, September 15, 2023,
    https://toronto.citynews.ca/2023/09/15/11000-ontarians-died-
    waiting-surgeries/.

3   World Health Organization. Declaration of Alma-Ata (Geneva:
    World Health Organization, 1978), https://apps.who.int/iris/
    handle/10665/347879.

4   "Primary care" and "primary health care" are similar terms
    but there are important differences. I have not discussed
    the distinctions in the text—but simply put, primary care
    is about service delivery, whereas primary health care is a
    broader term that includes population and public health.

5   Susan B. Rifkin, "Alma Ata after 40 Years: Primary Health Care and Health for All—From Consensus to Complexity," *BMJ Global Health* 3, suppl. 3 (December 2018). doi:10.1136/bmjgh-2018-001188.

6   Barbara Starfield et al., "Contribution of Primary Care to Health Systems and Health," *Milbank Quarterly* 83, no. 3 (2005): 457–502. doi:10.1111/j.1468-0009.2005.00409.x.

7   "Primary Care," World Health Organization, n.d., https://www. who.int/teams/integrated-health-services/clinical-services-and-systems/primary-care.

8   Roosa Tikkanen et al., "International Health Care System Profiles: Netherlands," Commonwealth Fund, June 5, 2020, https://www. commonwealthfund.org/international-health-policy-center/ countries/netherlands.

9   Canadian Institute for Health Information, "Hospital Spending: Focus on the Emergency Department" (Ottawa: CIHI; 2020), https://www.cihi.ca/sites/default/files/document/hospital-spending-highlights-2020-en.pdf.

10 Ake Blomqvist and Rosalie Wyonch. "Health Teams and Primary Care Reform in Ontario: Staying the Course." *CD Howe Institute Commentary* 551 (2019).

11 Patricia A. Collins et al., "The Untold Story: Examining Ontario's Community Health Centres' Initiatives to Address Upstream Determinants of Health," *Healthcare Policy* 10, no. 1 (2014): 14–29. https://www.ncbi.nlm.nih.gov/pmc/articles/PMC4253893/.

12 Kamila Premji, Michael E. Green, Richard H. Glazier, Shahriar Khan, Susan E. Schultz, Maria Mathews, Steve Nastos, Eliot Frymire, and Bridget L. Ryan. "Characteristics of Patients Attached to Near-retirement Family Physicians: A Population-Based Serial Cross-Sectional Study in Ontario, Canada." *BMJ Open* 13, no. 12 (2023): e074120.

13 "Survey Data Explorer," Our Care, n.d., https://data.ourcare.ca/ all-questions.

14 Richard H. Glazier, Brandon M. Zagorski, and Jennifer Rayner, "Comparison of Primary Care Models in Ontario by Demographics, Case Mix and Emergency Department Use, 2008/09 to 2009/10," IC/ES, March 2012. https://www.ices.on.ca/publications/research-reports/comparison-of-primary-care-models-in-ontario-by-demographics-case-mix-and-emergency-department-use-2008-09-to-2009-10/.

15 Kiran, Tara, Rahim Moineddin, Alexander Kopp, and Richard H. Glazier. "Impact of team-based care on emergency department use." *The Annals of Family Medicine* 20, no. 1 (2022): 24-31.

16 "Rapport annuel de gestion 2021–2022," Ministère de la Santé et des Services sociaux (quebec.ca), https://publications.msss.gouv.qc.ca/msss/document-003510/?&date=DESC&sujet=rapport-annuel&critere=sujet.

17 A. Lukey et al., "Facilitating Integration Through Team-Based Primary Healthcare: A Cross-Case Policy Analysis of Four Canadian Provinces," *International Journal of Integrated Care* 21, no. 4 (2021): 12. https://pubmed.ncbi.nlm.nih.gov/34824561/.

18 Auditor General of Alberta, "Better Healthcare for Albertans," May 2017, https://www.oag.ab.ca/reports/bhc-report-may-2017/.

Chapter 2: From Promise to Practicalities

1 When my friend David Clements read a draft of this book, he told me this part reminded him of Kotter's 8-step change model. For more information, see J.P. Kotter, *Leading Change* (Boston, MA: Harvard Business Review Press, 1996).

2 Thuy-Nga (Tia) Pham and Tara Kiran, "More Than 6.5 Million Adults in Canada Lack Access to Primary Care," Healthy Debate, March 14, 2023, https://healthydebate.ca/2023/03/topic/millions-adults-lack-canada-primary-care/.

3 "After a "Decade of Decline" in Health Care, Canadians Not Convinced That Money Is Enough to Solve the Crisis,"

Angus Reid Institute, August 17, 2023, https://angusreid.org/cma-health-care-access-priorities-2023/.

4   Harry Clarke-Ezzidio, "NHS Investment Would 'Pay for Itself Fourteen Times Over,'" *New Statesman*, September 20, 2023, https://www.newstatesman.com/spotlight/economic-growth/2023/08/nhs-funding-economic-growth-pay-fourteen-times-over-nhs-confederation-cf.

5   Schneider v. The Queen, [1982] 2 S.C.R. 112, 142.

6   Michael J.L. Kirby and Marjory LeBreton, "The Health of Canadians—the Federal Role." Final Report of the Standing Senate Committee on Social Affairs, Science and Technology (Ottawa: Parliament of Canada, 2002), 6, https://sencanada.ca/en/content/sen/committee/372/soci/rep/repoct02vol6-e.

7   Roy J. Romanow, *Building on Values: The Future of Health Care in Canada* (Saskatoon, SK: Commission on the Future of Health Care in Canada, 2002), 53.

8   Canada, "Legislative Summary of Bill C-14," Library of Parliament, Research Publications, 42nd Parliament, 1st Session, April 21, 2016 (updated September 27, 2018), https://lop.parl.ca/sites/PublicWebsite/default/en_CA/ResearchPublications/LegislativeSummaries/421C14E.

9   "Regulations for the Monitoring of Medical Assistance in Dying: SOR/2018-166," Canada Gazette, Part II, vol. 152, no. 16 (July 27, 2018), https://canadagazette.gc.ca/rp-pr/p2/2018/2018-08-08/html/sor-dors166-eng.html.

10 Mollie Dunsmuir, "The Spending Power: Scope and Limitations" (Ottawa: Government of Canada, October 1991), https://publications.gc.ca/collections/Collection-R/LoPBdP/BP/bp272-e.htm.

11 Thomas Axworthy, "Tom Kent: A Life of Purpose," *Toronto Star*, November 17, 2011, https://www.thestar.com/opinion/

tom-kent-a-life-of-purpose/article_eca13878-1899-5247-88fe-
dd897fda8431.html.

12 Tom Kent, "Working Papers on the Federal Spending Power,"
    Institute of Intergovernmental Relations, School of Policy Study,
    Queen's University, Working Papers 2007, 4, https://www.
    queensu.ca/iigr/sites/iirwww/files/uploaded_files/Kent1.pdf.

13 "Shared Health Priorities," Canadian Institute for Health Inform-
    ation, n.d., https://www.cihi.ca/en/shared-health-priorities.

14 Kent, "Working Papers," 6.

15 Canada Health Act, R.S.C. 65, 1985, c. C-6, https://laws-lois.
    justice.gc.ca/PDF/C-6.pdf.

16 "Regulation Relating to a Municipal Regular GP Scheme,"
    Government of Norway, November 23, 2003, https://www.
    regjeringen.no/en/dokumenter/regulation-relating-to-a-
    municipal-regul/id420530/.

17 G.T. Doran, "There's a S.M.A.R.T. Way to Write Management's
    Goals and Objectives," *Management Review* 70, no. 11 (1981): 35–36.

18 "2018 RDOC National Resident Survey," Resident Doctors
    of Canada, n.d., 48, https://residentdoctors.ca/publications/
    national-resident-survey/nrs-2018/.

Chapter 3: Recovering a Species at Risk

1 Diana Duong and Lauren Vogel, "National Survey Highlights
   Worsening Primary Care Access," *Canadian Medical Association
   Journal* 195, no. 16 (2023), https://www.cmaj.ca/content/
   195/16/E592.

2 CaRMS R-1 Match Reports, Table 11: First Choice Discipline of CMG
   Applicants, https://www.carms.ca/data-reports/r1-data-reports/.

3 HealthForceOntario, "Ontario Health—Health Force Survey
   Results," August 2021.

4 "Research into Factors That Influence Practice Scope and Location of Queen's Family Medicine Peterborough-Kawartha Site Residents" (prepared for the Peterborough Ontario Health Team by Jennifer Harrington, Arising Collective), March 30, 2023.

5 "Number of Physicians and Nurses per 10,000 Population by Health Region, 2021," Canadian Institute for Health Information, March 30, 2023, https://www.cihi.ca/en/number-of-physicians-and-nurses-per-10000-population-by-health-region-2021.

6 "An Introduction to Problem-Based Learning in the Faculty of Health Sciences at McMaster University," n.d., https://srs-slp.healthsci.mcmaster.ca/wp-content/uploads/2022/08/pbl-introductory-article.pdf.

7 Credit for this innovation belongs to Dr. Anthony Sanfilippo, formerly Associate Dean of the MD Program at Queen's University, who shared the idea with me in 2021 and oversaw the first steps toward its implementation.

8 Andrew Helt, Twitter post, April 19, 2023, 12:21 a.m.

9 "Canadian Doctors Spend Over 18 Million Hours a Year on Unnecessary Administrative Work," CFIB, January 30, 2023, https://www.cfib-fcei.ca/en/media/canadian-doctors-spend-over-18-million-hours-a-year-on-unnecessary-administrative-work.

10 Ruth Lavergne et al, "Declining Comprehensiveness of Services Delivered by Canadian Family Physicians Is Not Driven by Early-Career Physicians," *Annals of Family Medicine* 21, no 2. (2023): 151–56. https://pubmed.ncbi.nlm.nih.gov/36973051/.

11 Lindsay Hedden et al., "Family Physician Perspectives on Primary Care Reform Priorities: A Cross-Sectional Survey," *Canadian Medical Association Journal Open* 6, no. 2 (2021): E466–73. https://pubmed.ncbi.nlm.nih.gov/33958382/.

12 Shantanu Nundy et al., "The Quintuple Aim for Health Care Improvement: A New Imperative to Advance Health Equity,"

Journal of the American Medical Association 327, no. 6 (2022): 521–22. https://jamanetwork.com/journals/jama/article-abstract/2788483.

13 Thomas Bodenheimer, Cynthia Haq, and Wilhelm Lehmann, "Continuity and Access in the Era of Part-Time Practice," *Annals of Family Medicine* 16, no. 4 (2018): 359–60. https://pubmed.ncbi. nlm.nih.gov/29987087/.

14 E.M. Roos, et al., "Outcomes Following the GLA:D Program for Patients with Symptomatic Knee and Hip Osteoarthritis in Denmark, Canada and Australia. A Longitudinal Analysis Including 28,370 Patients," *Osteoarthritis and Cartilage* 29, no. 4 (2021): S31–S32. https://pubmed.ncbi.nlm.nih.gov/33561542/.

15 Roosa Tikkanen et al., "International Health Care System Profiles: Israel," Commonwealth Fund, June 5, 2020, https:// www.commonwealthfund.org/international-health-policy-center/countries/israel.

Chapter 4: Hope

1 "Constitution," World Health Organization, n.d., https://www.who. int/about/governance/constitution. Accessed August 13, 2023.

2 Philippians 2:3,4 (New International Version).

3 "First Nations Wellness Continuum Framework," Thunderbird Partnership Foundation, n.d., https://thunderbirdpf.org/fnmwc.

4 Dr. Carol Hopkins, personal message to author, August 14, 2023: "I did lead the development of the FNMWC but I didn't do it alone. Dr. Brenda Restoule was a co-chair along with Dr. Tom Wong. I did lead and inspire the development of the Indigenous Wellness Framework which is where Hope Belonging Meaning and Purpose (HBMP) came from. Elder Jim Dumont and I presented HBMP at a national meeting organized to review and synthesize regional discussions, and it was there that HBMP received unanimous consent to be placed at the centre of the FNMWC."

5   This image may be viewed on the Thunderbird Partnership Foundation website: https://thunderbirdpf.org/fnmwc/.

6   Evie Steele, "Nancy Pelosi Talks Politics, Personal Faith in Discussion," *The Hoya*, March 31, 2023, https://thehoya.com/pelosi-talks-politics-personal-faith-in-discussion/.

Chapter 5: Belonging

1   "Attachment Disorders," American Academy of Child and Adult Psychiatry, January 2017, https://www.aacap.org/AACAP/Families_and_Youth/Facts_for_Families/FFF-Guide/Attachment-Disorders-085.aspx.

2   Susan Jaffe, "US Surgeon General: Loneliness Is a Public Health Crisis, *The Lancet* 401, no. 10388 (2023): 1560. https://pubmed.ncbi.nlm.nih.gov/37182524/.

3   U.S. Surgeon General, "Our Epidemic of Loneliness and Isolation: The U.S. Surgeon General's Advisory on the Healing Effects of Social Connection and Community," 2023, https://www.hhs.gov/sites/default/files/surgeon-general-social-connection-advisory.pdf.

4   Catherine Donnelly et al., "How Does a Naturally Occurring Retirement Community with Supportive Programming Impact Health Utilization?" *Canadian Association for Health Services and Policy Research Conference* (2021).

5   Catherine Donnelly, "Neighbours Helping Neighbours Age Well at Home," Queen's Health Sciences Research Talks Series, YouTube, 20:06, March 24, 2023, https://www.youtube.com/watch?v=gM2p9VF9CLg.

Chapter 6: Meaning

1   Helena Palmgren, "Meningococcal Disease and Climate," *Global Health Action* 2, no. 1 (2009). https://www.tandfonline.com/doi/full/10.3402/gha.v2i0.2061.

Chapter 7: Purpose

1 "Honouring Our Strengths: Culture as Intervention in Addictions Treatment Reference Guide," CAMH/CHIR, n.d., https://cyfn.ca/wp-content/uploads/2016/10/Honouring-our-strengths-Culture-as-treatment-resource-guide.pdf.

2 "The 50th Anniversary of Martin Luther King, Jr.'s 'What Is Your Life's Blueprint?'" *Beacon Broadside*, October 26, 2017, https://www.beaconbroadside.com/broadside/2017/10/the-50th-anniversary-of-martin-luther-king-jrs-what-is-your-lifes-blueprint.html#:~:text="Number%20one%20in%20your%20life%27s,feel%20that%20you%20have%20worth.

Chapter 8: Health beyond Medicine

1 Edward Ng and Hoazhen Zhang, "The Mental Health of Immigrants and Refugees," Statistics Canada, August 19, 2020, https://www150.statcan.gc.ca/n1/pub/82-003-x/2020008/article/00001-eng.htm.

2 "Life Expectancy at Birth, Total (Years): Niger," n.d., World Bank, https://data.worldbank.org/indicator/SP.DYN.LE00.IN?locations=NE.

3 Joe Hasell et al., "Poverty," Our World in Data, n.d., https://ourworldindata.org/poverty.

4 "Social Determinants of Health and Health Inequalities," Government of Canada, n.d., https://www.canada.ca/en/public-health/services/health-promotion/population-health/what-determines-health.html.

5 "National Health Expenditure Trends, 2022—Snapshot," Canadian Institute for Health Information, November 3, 2022, https://www.cihi.ca/en/national-health-expenditure-trends-2022-snapshot. Accessed May 28, 2023.

6 Fully one-quarter of our spending is on hospitals—the number-one line item—while doctors and drugs are tied for second place. Three-quarters of our health care spending is covered by public funds, through governments. A quarter of the costs are paid privately.

7 "Health Spending (indicator)," OECD, n.d. doi: 10.1787/8643de7e-en. Accessed on September 23, 2023.

8 "Review of Evidence for Health-Related Social Needs Interventions," Commonwealth Fund, n.d., https://www.commonwealthfund.org/sites/default/files/2019-07/COMBINED-ROI-EVIDENCE-REVIEW-7-1-19.pdf. Accessed September 9, 2023.

9 "Closing the Gap in a Generation: Health Equity Through Action on the Social Determinants of Health: Final Report of the Commission on Social Determinants of Health," World Health Organization, 2008, https://www.who.int/publications/i/item/WHO-IER-CSDH-08.1.

Chapter 9: The Sound of Silence

1 Some of the following paragraphs are adapted from a chapter I wrote for a textbook I co-edited with law professor Colleen Flood and others. See: Colleen Flood, Vanessa MacDonnell, and Jane Philpott, eds., *Vulnerable: The Law, Policy and Ethics of COVID-19* (Ottawa: University of Ottawa Press, 2020).

2 Chinua Achebe, *The Education of a British-Protected Child: Essays* (New York: Penguin Group, 2009), 93.

3 Achebe, *The Education of a British-Protected Child*, 95.

4 "Health Advocate: Definition," Royal College of Physicians and Surgeons of Canada, n.d., https://www.royalcollege.ca/ca/en/canmeds/canmeds-framework/canmeds-role-health-advocate.html.

5   Laurel Thatcher Ulrich, *Well-Behaved Women Seldom Make History* (New York: Knopf, 2007).

6   "Roy's Full Speech," *Sydney Morning Herald*, November 4, 2004, https://www.smh.com.au/national/roys-full-speech-20041104-gdk1qn.html.

7   Canadian Institute for Health Information, "The Impact of COVID-19 on Long-Term Care in Canada: Focus on the First 6 Months" (Ottawa: CIHI; 2021), https://www.cihi.ca/sites/default/files/document/impact-covid-19-long-term-care-canada-first-6-months-report-en.pdf.

8   "The Predictable Crisis of Covid in Canada's Long-Term Care Homes," *BMJ* 382 (2023). https://www.bmj.com/content/382/bmj-2023-075148/peer-review.

9   "The World Expected More of Canada," *BMJ* 382 (2023). https://www.bmj.com/content/382/bmj.p1634.

10 Christopher Kliewer et al., "Who May Be Literate? Disability and Resistance to the Cultural Denial of Competence," *American Educational Research Journal* 43, no. 2 (Summer 2006). https://journals.sagepub.com/doi/10.3102/00028312043002163.

Chapter 10: Land, Language, Lineage, Loved Ones

1   Highlights from the Report of the Royal Commission on Aboriginal Peoples," Government of Canada, n.d., https://www.rcaanc-cirnac.gc.ca/eng/1100100014597/1572547985018.

2   "Beyond 94: Truth and Reconciliation in Canada," CBC News, June 22, 2023, https://www.cbc.ca/newsinteractives/beyond-94/enact-child-welfare-legislation-that-establishes-national-standards-for-aboriginal-child-apprehension-and-custody-cases.

3   My chief of staff at the time was John Brodhead. I had four chiefs of staff over four years. The others were Geneviève Hinse, Rachel Doran, and Adam Carroll. Each was superb.

4   "Jordan's Principle," Government of Canada, n.d., https://
     www.sac-isc.gc.ca/eng/1568396042341/1568396159824.

5   "United Nations Declaration on the Rights of Indigenous
     Peoples," United Nations, October 2, 2007, 8. https://www.
     un.org/development/desa/indigenouspeoples/wp-content/
     uploads/sites/19/2018/11/UNDRIP_E_web.pdf.

6   "United Nations Declaration on the Rights of Indigenous
     Peoples," United Nations, October 2, 2007, 5. https://www.
     un.org/development/desa/indigenouspeoples/wp-content/
     uploads/sites/19/2018/11/UNDRIP_E_web.pdf.

7   "Notices and Requests Related to an Act Respecting First
     Nations, Indigenous and Métis Children, Youth and Families,"
     Government of Canada, n.d., https://www.sac-isc.gc.ca/eng/
     1608565826510/1608565862367.

Chapter 11: Nothing But Medicine Writ Large

1   E. Friedlander, "Rudolf Virchow on Pathology Education,"
     address to the Group for Research in Pathology Education
     (Hershey, PA, n.d.,), http://www.pathguy.com/virchow.htm.

Chapter 12: When Politics Works

1   "Criminal Justice," Canadian Substance Use Costs and Harms,
     n.d., https://csuch.ca/substance-use-costs/criminal-justice/.
     Accessed July 31, 2023.

2   "Evidence Around Harm Reduction and Public Health–Based
     Drug Policies, Canadian Drug Policy Coalition, https://www.
     drugpolicy.ca/resources/evidence/. Accessed July 31, 2023.

3   "Canadian Supervised Injection Sites," Government of Canada
     (data blog), last updated October 6, 2023, https://health-infobase.
     canada.ca/datalab/supervised-consumption-sites-blog.html.
     Accessed July 2, 2023.

4   James D. Livingston, "Supervised Consumption Sites and Crime: Scrutinizing the Methodological Weaknesses and Aberrant Results of a Government Report in Alberta, Canada," *Harm Reduction Journal* 18, no. 4 (2021). https://doi.org/10.1186/s12954-020-00456-2.

5   Austin Frakt, "Pointers from Portugal on Addiction and the Drug War," *New York Times*, October 5, 2020, https://www.nytimes.com/2020/10/05/upshot/portugal-drug-legalization-treatment.html. Accessed July 2, 2023.

6   Harm Reduction International, "Harm Reduction in Switzerland" (London: HRI, 2022), https://hri.global/wp-content/uploads/2022/11/Harm-Reduction-in-Switzerland_FINAL.pdf.

7   Travis Lupick, tweet, September 13, 2017, 8:55 p.m.

Chapter 13: Using Clinical Skills in Politics

1   Elizabeth Thompson, "Newly Elected MPs Unclear on Their Jobs and Lack Training: Study," iPolitics, November 30, 2010, https://www.ipolitics.ca/news/mps-unclear-on-their-jobs-and-lack-training-study.

2   "Key Leadership Competency Profile and Examples of Effective and Ineffective Behaviours," Government of Canada, last modified June 7, 2016, https://www.canada.ca/en/treasury-board-secretariat/services/professional-development/key-leadership-competency-profile/examples-effective-ineffective-behaviours.html. Accessed August 2, 2023.

3   Mark D. Aronson, "The Purpose of the Medical Record: Why Lawrence Weed Still Matters," *American Journal of Medicine* 132, no. 11 (2019): 1256–57.

4   "September 2023 Rentals.ca Report," Rentals.ca, October 13, 2023, https://rentals.ca/blog/september-2023-rentals-ca-report.

5   Rob Carrick, "Young Adults Are Giving Up on Home Ownership, and a Lot of Them Are Furious about It," *Globe and Mail*, May 3, 2023, https://www.theglobeandmail.com/investing/personal-finance/article-young-adults-are-giving-up-on-home-ownership-and-a-lot-of-them-are/.

6   "Estimating How Much Housing We'll Need by 2030," CMHC, September 13, 2023, https://www.cmhc-schl.gc.ca/blog/2023/estimating-how-much-housing-we-need-by-2030.

7   Ursula M. Vogl et al., "Lack of Consensus Identifies Important Areas for Future Clinical Research: Advanced Prostate Cancer Consensus Conference (APCCC) 2019 Findings," *European Journal of Cancer* 160 (2022): 24–60. doi: 10.1016/j.ejca.2021.09.036.

8   There is a fascinating book about how politicians must learn this art—for the sake of democracy. It is called *The Persuaders: At the Front Lines of the Fight for Hearts, Minds, and Democracy*, and is written by Anand Giridharadas (New York: Penguin Random House, 2022). It includes an important message to all of us about the risks of writing people off simply because we don't all see the world in the same way.

9   Holly McKenzie-Sutter, "'Anti-Vaxxer Mobs' Can't Dictate Policy in Canada, Trudeau Says of Campaign Protests," *Globe and Mail*, September 6, 2021, https://www.theglobeandmail.com/politics/article-liberal-leader-justin-trudeau-pledges-legal-protection-for-businesses/.

10   Owen Dyer, "Covid-19: Unvaccinated Face 11 Times Risk of Death from Delta Variant, CDC Data Show," *British Medical Journal* (2021). https://doi.org/10.1136/bmj.n2282.

11   Hudson Birden et al., "Defining Professionalism in Medical Education: A Systematic Review," *Medical Teacher* 36, no. 1 (2014): 47–61. https://pubmed.ncbi.nlm.nih.gov/24252073/.

12 "The House of Commons and Its Members," in *House of Commons Procedure and Practice*, Third Edition, ed. Marc Bosc and André Gagnon (Ottawa: Government of Canada, 2017), https://www.ourcommons.ca/procedure/procedure-and-practice-3/ch_04_9-e.html.

13 Canada, House of Commons Debates, October 6, 2016, https://www.ourcommons.ca/DocumentViewer/en/42-1/house/sitting-89/hansard#Int-9147950.

14 Robin V. Sears, "The Delicate Craft of Caucus Management," *Toronto Star*, March 24, 2019, https://www.thestar.com/opinion/star-columnists/2019/03/24/the-delicate-craft-of-caucus-management.html.

15 Bo Emerson, "Joanne Rogers and the world according to Fred," *Atlanta Journal-Constitution*, January 15, 2021, https://www.ajc.com/life/joanne-rogers-and-the-world-according-to-fred/ZIQMJQQLUFA7DJDL7WIXR62Y3Y/

Chapter 14: The Parable of the Crumbling Cottage

1 André Picard, "In Our Politics and Our Health Care, the Price of Dithering in Canada Is Structural Decay," *Globe and Mail*, June 12, 2023, https://www.theglobeandmail.com/opinion/article-in-our-politics-and-our-health-care-the-price-of-dithering-in-canada/.

2 "Canadians Outline Their 2023 Federal Budget Priorities," Ipsos, March 27, 2023, https://www.ipsos.com/en-ca/canadians-outline-their-2023-federal-budget-priorities. Accessed July 8, 2023; David Coletto, "Conservatives Lead by 10 Before Cabinet Shuffle," Abacus Data, July 26, 2023, https://abacusdata.ca/conservatives-lead-by-10-on-the-heels-of-the-federal-cabinet-shuffle. Accessed July 28, 2023.

3   "Health Care Surpasses Inflation as Top National Issue of
    Concern: Nanos," CTV News, December 1, 2022, https://
    www.ctvnews.ca/health/health-care-surpasses-inflation-as-
    top-national-issue-of-concern-nanos-1.6176739. Accessed
    July 8, 2023.

4   Statistics Canada, "Distributions of Household Economic
    Accounts for Income, Consumption, Saving and Wealth of
    Canadian Households, First Quarter 2023," The Daily, July 4,
    2023, https://www150.statcan.gc.ca/n1/daily-quotidien/230704/
    dq230704a-eng.htm. Accessed August 12, 2023.

5   Joe Hasell et al., "Economic Inequality," Our World in Data,
    2023, https://ourworldindata.org/economic-inequality.
    Accessed August 9, 2023.

Epilogue

1   Monique Bégin, *Ladies, Upstairs! My Life in Politics and After*
    (Montreal: McGill-Queen's University Press, 2019).

2   Bégin, *Ladies, Upstairs!*, 235.

3   Bégin, *Ladies, Upstairs!*, 236.

4   Bégin, *Ladies, Upstairs!*, 267.

5   Frederick Zimmerman and Nathaniel Anderson, "Trends in
    Health Equity in the United States by Race/Ethnicity, Sex,
    and Income, 1993–2017,"*JAMA Network Open* 2, no. 6 (2019),
    https://jamanetwork.com/journals/jamanetworkopen/
    fullarticle/2736934.

Index

Department of Indian Affairs and
Northern Development, 159
Department of Indian and Inuit
Services, 160
Department of Indigenous Services
Canada, 161–162, 165
DePaul, Dr. Vincent, 107
Diefenbaker, John (PM), 59, 236
Dignitas International, 178
disabilities: advocating for, 151–155,
157; and child welfare, 168–169;
and COVID-19, 145–157; and
primary care access, 14, 80
doctors *see* family doctors/medicine;
health workers
Donnelly, Dr. Catherine, 107
Douglas, Tommy (Premier), 21, 22, 59,
236
Dr. Peter Centre (Vancouver)
(supervised consumption site), 197
drug and substance use: Bill C-37,
197; cannabis decriminalization,
191–194; causes, 15, 101, 189, 200;
and chronic pain, 15, 189; deaths/
statistics, 47, 194–195, 201–202, 205;
harm reduction, 189–191, 195–198,
200–201, 203–204; heroin-assisted
therapy (HAT), 200–201, 204;
international policies, 198–200,
202–203; opioid policies, 189–191,
194–198, 201–204; overdoses, 190,
194, 197, 201–203, 205; and social
support, 189, 197, 199, 203
Dumas, Arlen, 161
Dumont, Jim, 127

E

economics *see* funding, health care;
income
education: as human right, 137, 242;
Indigenous, 161; international,
36, 121, 178; public, as model for

primary care systems, 19, 33, 57–58,
77–78, 82, 242; as social determinant
of health, 3, 94, 133, 139, 140–141
education, medical: admissions
process, 68, 72; bias against family
medicine, 62–63, 68; clinical skills
taught, 209–213, 215–216, 217–218,
219–221, 222–223, 227–228; as
competency-based, 209; innovation/
reform, 70–74, 82–83
electronic medical record (EMR), 23,
69, 77
emergency departments: and COVID-
19, 13, 156; and lack of primary care
access, 14–16, 23, 31, 41–42, 81; staff
shortages, 14, 15–16, 18, 62, 235
employment: as human right, 137; as
social determinant of health, 139,
141
Ethiopia *see also* Africa, 36, 121, 178, 181
Evans, Dr. John, 71

F

faith, and mental/spiritual health,
89–91, 95–98, 113–114, 116–117
family doctors/medicine *see also*
health workers; nurses/nurse-
practitioners (NPs); primary care
homes; autonomy of, 69, 74–75;
burnout/exhaustion of, 18, 62–63,
66, 74, 128–129, 235, 251; capitation
payment model, 27–30; Community
Health Centres (CHCs), 27, 31, 80;
decline in/retirement of, 62–63;
educational bias against, 62–63,
68–70; educational reform, 70–74,
82–83; Family Health Teams (FHTs),
27, 31–32; fee-for-service model,
26–27, 79, 81; and gender-based
discrimination, 68; job satisfaction
of, 79–80, 248; and patient
relationships, 64–67, 219–220;